BUSTA RHYME

I SHUFFLE THROUGH MY MIND
TO SEE IF I CAN FIND
THE WORDS I LEFT BEHIND
- GREEN DAY

TEEN SPIRIT

Edited By Sarah Washer

First published in Great Britain in 2017 by:

Coltsfoot Drive
Peterborough
PE2 9BF
Telephone: 01733 890066
Website: www.youngwriters.co.uk

FOREWORD

Welcome, Reader, to 'Busta Rhyme – Teen Spirit'.

For Young Writers' latest poetry competition, we asked our writers to wow us with their words and bust out their bard side!

The result is this collection of fantastic poetic verse that covers a whole host of different topics. Get ready to be blown away by these passionate poems about love and relationships, school and bullying, equality and human rights, and demanding day-to-day issues that come with living in today's society. This collection has a poem to suit everyone.

Whereas the majority of our writers chose to express themselves with a free verse style, others gave themselves the challenge of other techniques such as acrostics and rhyming couplets.

There was a great response to this competition which is always nice to see, and the standard of entries was excellent, therefore I'd like to say a big thank you and well done to everyone who entered.

I hope you enjoy reading these poems as much as I did.

Keep writing!
Sarah Washer

CONTENTS

Kesteven & Grantham Girls' School, Grantham

Elizabeth Proctor (15)	56
Alexandra Tyndall (15)	58
Eleanor Massey (13)	60
Cara Booth (12)	62
Shannon Beasor (15)	63
Sumitra Patel (11)	64

Lady Manners School, Bakewell

Daisy Rogers (15)	65
Isabel Lovell (15)	66
Emma Gwynne Ann Pugh (15)	69

Largs Academy, Largs

Abbie Franklin (14)	71

Lodge Park Academy, Corby

Cerys Robertson (13)	73
Connor Neill (13)	74
Shanade Bisland (14)	76
Ana Jefimova (13)	78
Katie Erridge (13)	80
Kai Campbell (13)	82
Samantha Annabel Balcomb (13)	83
Dylan Muir (13)	84
Kimran Kaur Singh (13)	85
Chloe Ann Scott (13)	86
Maisie Stevenson (13)	87
Kaden Carr (13)	88
Rhys Rutter (13)	89
Charley Choina (13)	90
Catherine Clayton (13)	91
Amy Dawn Gallagher (13)	92

Luton Sixth Form College, Luton

Leah Marie Smith (17)	93
Karolina Zadroga (17)	94
Fiona Green (17)	97

Shamia Khan (16)	99

Mearns Academy, Laurencekirk

Cameron Stewart (11)	101
Morgan Le-Tekro (12)	102
Harry Coleman (11)	104
Ella Geddes (12)	105
Rhianna Grace Morgan (12)	106
Erin Hair (12)	107
Josie King (12)	108
Kirsty Gellatly (11)	109
Robyn Jane Fowlie (12)	110
Erin Spence (12)	111
Alex Clarke (11)	112
Cameron Barclay (12)	113
Max Miller (12)	114

Outwood Academy Newbold, Chesterfield

Caitlin Lewis (11)	115
Bailey Ethan Astle (14)	116
Bethany Louise Parsons (14)	118
Abigail Khan (16)	119
Ciara Davies (17)	120
Nyesha Davies-Collis (12)	121

Redborne Upper School & Community College, Ampthill

Phoebe Taylor (13)	122
Lauren Campbell (16)	124
Archie Walker-Merison (13)	126
Lucy Gouldthorpe (16)	128
Megan Kemeny-Ruff (16)	130
Rory McGowan (17)	131
Georgia Cope (17)	132
Emily Campbell (16)	134
Hollie Hansen (16)	136
Colette Joy Russell (13)	138
Maizie Sherwood (15)	139
Toby Smith (13)	140
Lara Denise Fisher (17)	141

Edie Wright (13)	142
David Fussell (13)	143
Olivia Thomas (16)	144
Sofia Villa-Buil (13)	145
Amy Scott (13)	146
Kade Alford (13)	147
Maddy Jenny Chesham (13)	148
Debbie Fridkin (13)	149
Corren Perks (18)	150
Ellie Camp (18)	151
Ben Seber (13)	152
Fraser Lamb (14)	153
Kaiya Kaltio (17)	154
Reece Collins (13)	155
Ella Cope (13)	156
Harvey Sweetland Jones (13)	157
Nathan Eaves (12)	158
Jasmin Susan Clark Batchelor (13)	159
Luke Smith (18)	160
Nathan Wing (13)	161
Connor Andrews (13)	162
Sofia Samm (13)	163
Rhiannah Webster (14)	164
Tia Lawrence (13)	165
Tyler Swain (13)	166
Christopher Dadd (13)	167
Kate Devonshire (13)	168
Harvey Turner (14)	169
Joshua Tuuk (13)	170
Henry Treanor (14)	171

St Paul's Catholic School, Leicester

Jadesola Bejide (14)	172
Rosa-Mei Wright (12)	175
Tendo Gumbo (15)	176
Umar Patel (12)	179
Aiden Clayton-Crosse (14)	180
Greta Kaur-Taylor (14)	182
Adam Nemat Bhatti (13)	184
Rhiannon Kennedy (13)	186
Chantelle Nyasha Giwa (13)	188

St Peter's Independent School, Northampton

Charlotte Schofield (12)	189
Max Miller (13)	190
Takudzwa Mshayavanhu (12)	191
Keisha Dera (11)	192
Devlin Cattermole (11)	193

The Kibworth High School, Leicester

Jessica Smith (12)	194
Laura Smith (14)	196
Sophie Grove (14)	198
Rachel Danielle Modha (14)	200
Rowan Guy (13)	201
Emily Bettinson (12)	202
Louise Kyle (12)	203
Hannah Davey (12)	204
LJ Hensman (15)	205
Mbaweme Zimba (14)	206
Ben Sturgess (13)	207
Eliza Parsons (12)	208
Andrew Constantinou (12)	209
Rebecca Humphrey (12)	210

Westbourne Academy, Ipswich

Demi Hart (12)	211
Bailey Devereux (12), Freddie King (12) & Taylor Bullard (12)	212
Samuel Bell (12)	214

THE POEMS

Different

You don't know me
Yet you hate me
I can see it in your eyes
I'm a creature
I'm a monster
I'm something you despise

You'll never hear
You'll never know
The words I choose to say
You chew them up
And spit them out in a bitter, twisted way

I mustn't argue
I cannot fight
There's nothing I can do
You're in the wrong
You just smile
They always believe you

Is it because I'm different?
Even though I am the same?
My blood is red
The same as yours
Yet colour is to blame.

Eliza Reid (15)

Female Stereotypes ABC

A is for astronaut and other typical man jobs,
B is for being dramatic or snobs,
C is for cleaning all around the house,
D is for dresses or a pretty blouse,
E is for eating habits and being
Fussy with food,
G is for girly girls and all being good,
H is for heels with their abnormal height,
I is for the pushed away ideas from men,
J is for the men's jobs seen on paper and pen,
K is for the knitting and the elderly's hobbies,
L is for being laughed at for certain industries,
M can be the make-up to be recognisable,
Never can you wear a dress without it being special,
Only a man could go to the gym without losing weight,
Pink can only be worn by girls under eight,
The Queen, our leader, doesn't carry the stereotype,
Remember Amelia Earhart, she seemed all right,
Seems to be that the people who can
Turn events in history are not judged by a man,
U is for understanding, which I hope will happen soon, that
Variety in females is not thin or fat,
'Weak women' is not an actual fact, but
eXisting stereotypes could end quickly
Yet people won't know about it until other people copy me
And finally Z is for zero stereotypes left.

Kate Robinson (13)

Belmont Academy, Ayr

Remember

Remember that day a few years ago,
We went to the park and then it started to snow.
We played in the garden until the sun had gone down
Making snowmen and dragons and even a snow town.

Do you remember that night when we slept by the river,
I gave you my coat when you started to shiver.
The tent had collapsed so we slept under the stars,
When you think of how we used to be we have come so far.

Remember those weeks when I slept outside your door,
To protect you from the monsters that lived under the floor.
And all those long, long walks in the woods,
When we pretended to be knights or wizards, just by putting
up our hoods.

Remember how we would laugh and giggle and smile
Remember the games we would play by the stile.
Whenever you cry and things look bad,
Whenever you can't help feeling stressed or sad.

Simply remember how simple and easy life used to be,
Remember when the right and the wrong were easy to see.

Remember who we both used to be.

Harriet Mirtle (14)
Belmont Academy, Ayr

Baton Twirling, An Olympic Sport?

B aton twirling, an Olympic sport?
A bnormal you might say,
T he idea might come out the wrong way,
O r it will sound OK,
N ever think it is not hard.

T he combination of different sports,
W e have the leg strength of a runner,
I n sync we will always be,
R eflexes of a fencer,
L eotards and sparkly costumes, you will always see.
I have the dance technique of rhythmic gymnastics
N ever will I fail to compete
G ood legs and pointed feet.

A erials are always important,
N o drop performances are always the best.

O ver-clapping from the audience,
L oud screams of excitement,
Y es it might seem different,
M ay think it is complete nonsense
P ut those feelings away...
I t incorporates all the sports,
C ombination, you might say

S port of all sports,
P otential as an Olympic sport
O r just a bunch of rubbish?
R achel just proved it is only right
T wirling *should* be an Olympic sport.

Rachel Gilchrist (12)

Belmont Academy, Ayr

Can't I Be Me?

You don't have to be scared,
You have never been impaired,
Now just be you
And let's create a breakthrough.

L et's be honest, that now I am at my strongest, I have something to say, that had to come out one day.
G oing straight out with it, so please don't throw a fit, but now it's time, for me to finish this climb.
B eginning to end, it's been hard to pretend, I just can't do it anymore, it's time to open the door.
T his is me, and I'm in love with a he, sorry I didn't say, I'm gay.

Some in society condemn when a woman kisses a woman,
Or when a man holds a man,
But people are people,
Why don't we get treated equal?

LGBT have rights,
So there is no need for fights,
Why not be smart
And follow our hearts?

Jodie Storrie (13)
Belmont Academy, Ayr

Help...

Falling, falling deep, deep down,
Not physical but mental, into your own mind.
The monster stalks you day and night,
Staying out of anyone's sight.
You can't get free and there's no real cure.
It tells you that you're useless, ugly and fat.
They tell you that it's lying, but you can't be sure.
Sometimes you are angry, but most of the time sad,
Scared you'll lose all your friends because they think you're mad.
You might be feeling great today, but you're constantly afraid,
That at some point it's going to raise its ugly head.
You just want to cry and cry,
Most of the time you're not sure why,
Feeling bad about yourself,
Wanting to take the razor from that shelf
And press it to your thigh.
And as you bleed all you can see, is depression's evil glee.

Grace Seaton White (12)
Belmont Academy, Ayr

Without Music

Without music
What would this world be?
Just deafening silence
Void of all melody.

It is simple but complex
The lyrics take time.
Some are just music,
Others have rhyme.

So many songs
Some are brand new
But many are old
We all know one or two.

Commercial jingles that get suck in your head,
Relaxing tunes for heading to bed.
Holiday songs played one month a year
Electronic beats, pleasing to the ear.
Wild rock and roll, rebellious and loud
Crazy singers, jumping into the crowd.
Wedding bells, for when the time is right
Down the aisle all dressed in white.
Smooth jazz with piano and sax
Easy listening so you can relax.
Lullabies from when you were small,
Incredibly different, but I love them all!

Rose Saville (12)
Belmont Academy, Ayr

Suicide

She sits on the oak swing waiting for the rain to drown her,
Leaves fall from the tree landing neatly on her hair,
She tightens the scarf around her neck,
Watching each season fly,
People would walk by and not spare a glance,
She knows the reason but they refuse to admit it,
She sits on the swing all day, never to leave,
The first day she came here she hung herself from the tree,
A lonely boy wanders through the meadow,
Accepting death in the place of life,
Hurtful words covered his face,
The little boy skipped his way over to the oak tree,
Placing a flower he picked, on the ground below the girl's feet,
She eyed the boy carefully as tears came to his eyes,
She knew no other,
This boy, her dead brother.

Kirsty Walker (14)
Belmont Academy, Ayr

Poverty

No one should be alone in this world,
We should all try,
To help boys and girls,
Too poor to cry.

If you don't have much money,
We will try and help,
We don't think it's funny,
We won't give you the belt.

We shall never give up,
Everyone cares about you,
We will give you some water in a cup,
Soon there will only be few.

Don't worry, everyone falls,
But we will pick you up again,
We shall give you a call,
And you won't be in pain.

We will give you some food,
If you can't afford,
We will put you in a good mood,
You won't be bored!

Kara Margaret Lindsay (13)
Belmont Academy, Ayr

Where Did All The Animals Go?

Precious puppies, farmed for money.
Helpless hens, kept inside when it's sunny.

Terrific tigers, skinned for coats.
Wondrous whales, harpooned from boats.

Perfect polar bears, with nowhere to hunt.
Beautiful bears, that have died in a stunt.

Lovely leopards, killed out in the sun.
Curious cheetahs, with nowhere to run.

Loopy lions, kept in a cage.
Gorgeous gorillas, killed in a rage.

Dancing dolphins, caught in a net.
Menacing monkeys, not a suitable pet.

Elegant elephants, shot in a row.
Delicate deer, killed with a bow.

Isla Cummings (13)
Belmont Academy, Ayr

The Wondering Poet

I wonder: what's love?
Is it the way I feel when you say my name or
Is it the way you care for me even when I am not there?
Is it the way you treat my wounds
Even when we are apart?

For me love is: being yours and you being mine
The feelings I feel when I hear your name.
Also, it's sunshine in the middle of rainy day
And it is all the little things that I would be terrified
To tell anyone
But you.

Ivana Drdakova (18)
Boston College, Boston

The Sound Of Silence

Silence is a mirage,
Silence is a vision,
It comes; it goes,
Silence is a mirage.

Silence is fleeting, hear:
The rustling of the leaves,
The clicking of the pen,
The pitter-patter of the rain.

Silence is fleeting, hear:
The shutting of the door,
The creaking of the gate,
The banging of the cupboard.

Silence is fleeting, hear:
The whistling of the kettle,
The ticking of the clock,
The screaming of the alarm.

It's hard to find silence,
You can always hear
A small little sound
That escalates in silence.

But when you finally
Find silence,
You can hear your heartbeat
Beating and pulsing through your heart.

Isabel Last (12)
Dereham Neatherd High School, Dereham

What Is Beauty?

What is the definition of beautiful?
Photoshopped women in magazines?
Natural beauty is beautiful.
Faces caked in tonnes of make-up.
A fake vision of yourself.
It's not you!
You're not fat, you have a bold shape.
You're not thin, you have a small figure.
You don't need a membership, you don't need to pay
Be happy the way you are, you are perfect.

Sophie Baird-Parker (12)

Dereham Neatherd High School, Dereham

Who Are We?

So who are you?
Who am I?

What language do you speak?
Scottish or is it English or is it Australian or Canadian?
Arabic or Chinese or Setswana or Romanian?
Everyone speaks!

It doesn't matter where you come from,
Somewhere warm or cold,
If you're from a desert or a snowy glacier.
North, south, east or west Africa, Europe or Asia,
We all live on the same planet!

Doesn't matter if you have a big family or a small one.
If you live together or apart.
If you have one cousin or 100.
Family is family,
Everyone has someone.

It doesn't matter what you look like,
If you're as tall as a skyscraper
Or as small as a mouse,
If your eyes are blue, green or brown,
If you look happy, sad or show no emotion at all,
We are all human.

So who are you?
Who am I?

Poppy Watson (12)
Dornoch Academy, Dornoch

A Side Order Of Equality

In 1865, the Civil War was fought,
For the right against racial discrimination,
Blood was shed from black and white,
Yet the blood was always red.

The battle ended, North against South,
But still discrimination creeps the land,
Many of us stand for equality,
A battle spanning time.

One ninety years later,
There is shame on our country,
The blood is in the paper,
McDonald's has been sued for racial discrimination.

McD's is denying the evidence that's clear,
10 workers were insulted, race at heart,
Replaced by white workers, due to complaints,
Stand up and be counted, don't stand behind your golden arches.

In Virginia, in 2013,
The food giant insulted the colour of ten,
Do they have this right to colour our counters,
All I wanted was fast food with a side order of equality.

Big Mac, you rot my guts,
Twist my brain,
The multi-million pound company turned back time,
And fed the virus racism.

We all want to live,
We all want to grow,
No man is above,
No colour should be kept behind.

The master of money leads the way,
From President Lincoln to this date,
Our belief is strong, the belief of right,
But we battle on, for our families and those who have died.

Hannah Grewcock (12)
Dornoch Academy, Dornoch

Equal Rights

People always say the world has equal rights
And this topic has started a lot of fights.

The LGBT community receives little respect
And the little they do get is rather indirect.

Disabled people don't get the access they require,
Which leads to them having to permanently retire.

Women are treated like lower life forms
The vote, politics, education are torn.

Racism is strong even to this day,
Victimisation is all I have to say.

This needs to change.

Pixie Murray (11)
Dornoch Academy, Dornoch

She

She runs to me, broken and distressed
Jaw set in anger, her hair a mess
Asking for help she pleads and cries
She spouts a story, all deception and lies
Her boyfriend, abuse, a sharp blow to the head
Whispering, she hisses, 'I'm better off dead.'

She sees me again, this time on her face
Lies a bruise on her cheek, her neck out of place
Asking for help, she pleads and cries
Her tissue dabbing at tear-stained eyes
Her boyfriend, abuse, a kick to the chest
Close now, she whispers, 'It's what he does best.'

She calls my name, her voice all hoarse,
'It's not him, it's me,' full of remorse
Still asking for help, she pleads and cries
Colour drains from her face, a final goodbye
Her boyfriend, abuse, a punch to her spleen
Leaving, she speaks, 'Please say it's a dream.'

I'm the girl in the mirror and this is what I see
A girl who just wants to live and be free
But that cannot happen for society states
That the world is a darkening, terrible place
For that reason, the only reason there could be
I am that girl and she is me.

Molly Jamieson (14)
Dumfries Academy, Dumfries

Untitled

Their worlds are similar to yours and mine,
Just a boy who walks up with a smile,
He says that he doesn't want to be a boy,
Says that he doesn't care for the blue toys,
His mum doesn't understand,
Says that he's been infected by the news,
Infected by all the choice,
'There are only two genders,' she says,
As she walks away with a frown on her face,
She'll never understand, he thinks,
As he walks towards the kitchen sink,
Not knowing that Val next door was thinking the same,
As her father insults her for being gay,
'You're a disgrace to the family name!' he screams,
But all Val can see are her fears,
As her Beagle walks near,
Shoving her hand for comfort,
As her exterior grew tougher,
Her mind shattered,
She thought that her reputation would be tattered,
And so did Dave,
Who has been suffering depression,
His friends say that he never changes his expression,
As the plants lay strewn on the floor,
Everything scattered with petals and thorns,
He cries taking the pills,

All he can think of is the window sill,
Rae thought they were all the same,
The trans, the mentally unwell and the gays,
She thought they all made it up,
Just so their friends never gave them up,
She never knew how much words hurt,
As she walked up to her boyfriend Kurt,
She thought she needed to break up with him,
For the fact he was polyamorous,
She thought he was untrustworthy,
When the truth was he couldn't help who he loved,
And still the trauma occurs,
All the insults and the slurs,
For all the ones who can't change who they are,
And for all who just love who they love,
Their worlds aren't all that different to ours,
Apart from all the hours,
They spent wishing they weren't who they are.

Rhea Donaldson (14)
Dumfries Academy, Dumfries

Things Boys Will Never Understand

The things that boys will never understand
Is the way of the look
Or touch of a hand
Short tops is all they see
It's just a game, you and me.

They talk to us like we're all they want
And ask for things we haven't got
They do things that don't make sense
I thought you liked me
Is this the end?

'You knew this would come at the end of the day.'
'You're not what I'm looking for,' is what they'll say.
'Let's go on break
So I can think things through.'
What if I think I'm devoted to you?

But in an hour they're talking to someone new
In a week it will be a few
What's been left
Isn't us
It's just me and you.

I see you walk with her
Is it always a game?
You use girls as a rise to fame.

I hope you know they're not all the same
Some don't treat us like a game
I hope you know
It won't cause you pain
To raise your game.

Find a man who can treat you right
It isn't always a mighty fight
Just because I cried at night
Doesn't mean I'm weak
I won't give up the right
To find a man who will stand by me for life.

Hannah Hall (14)

Dumfries Academy, Dumfries

Can We?

Can we not just let this go? Come on, it's not that big a deal.
Dirty looks and mind games, I don't really see the appeal.
Statuses and screenshots repeating words said,
Spreading rumours and secrets behind backs and turned heads.
Trying our best to make the others feel low,
But seriously, please can we not let this go?

Because I'm sick of these ongoing competitions of cold shoulder,
Throwing sticks, stones and sentences, can we not act a bit older?
Misunderstandings and difference of opinions,
Have caused life-ending wars and devastated millions.
But fine then, all right, you just keep making a show,
But come on now please, I want to let this go!

But we are human and we're stubborn and we're greedy and we're proud,
Refusing to bury the hatchet or make amends out loud.
We choose to live in ignorance,
No space for any difference.
We'd rather stay oblivious
And it's really quite ridiculous.
Raised voices demanding explanations,
While roaring accusations.
Unwilling to apologise
Or even just to compromise.

But we're human and we're selfish and we're cruel and we are low,
But just this once for our own sake, can we please just let this go?

Cara Anne McGregor (14)

Dumfries Academy, Dumfries

Blame

We were never allowed ambition
Stay in the kitchen is the tradition
But recently our rights have changed
We got the vote but also the blame
We felt empowered, with our heads held high
We walked the streets feeling alive.

But they were there waiting while we walked home
We were scared, we pretended we were on the phone
Looking us up and down and there was their chance
But only one look, no second glance
A vulnerable girl, only young
Onto each other that's where they clung.

Then school came along, people found out
All the names you can think of they would shout,
'Pull down your skirt or it will happen again.'
'Was this your only chance of fame?'
She'd hide away at lunch to avoid the shame.

How could you do that, she was only a kid?
You're dirty, disgusting, it's stuck in her head
Why isn't our world such a safe place
For all the girls of such a young age?

Kirsty Adamson (14)
Dumfries Academy, Dumfries

Triggered!

It's the year 2016
and the world is full of edgy teens,
who make drinking bleach and suicide look like a meme.
The community of LBGTs is getting bigger and bigger,
and more and more people are getting very triggered!
When you're a teen, your emotions are
spinning round like the wheels of a car,
and slowly, slowly, I start to see
that everybody is changing around me.
The rise of social media
causes mass hysteria
and as social media keeps getting bigger,
more and more people keep getting triggered.
Some of the edgy teens are edgy because they are:
on the edge of suicide,
on the edge of thin ice
and they can't decide
whether they should live or die.
Some people say that 'bigger is better and better is bigger',
But I'm sitting here saying,
'I'm triggered!'

Evan Biesek (14)
Dumfries Academy, Dumfries

I Am Me

Who am I?
Should I be like you?
Should I look the same?
Think and act like you do?

I am me.

I am my warm brown eyes,
My freckled nose,
My scrapes and scars
From bumps and blows.

I am me.

I am my awkward smile,
My laugh, my accent,
What I say.
What my words meant.

I am me.

I am my scraped Doc Martens,
My ripped-up jeans,
My passion, my style,
That's all me.

I am me.

I am my music playlist,
The songs I sing,
My tunes, my jam,
The concerts I see.

I am me.

I am not your flawless make-up,
Your on-fleek brows,
Your wardrobe, your hair,
Your thoughts, your feelings, your hopes and cares.

I am me.

Cait Notman (13)
Dumfries Academy, Dumfries

Beauty

Beauty is only skin deep
Don't try and say
It's what's on the inside that counts
When that's not the case
Everyone only notices your face,
You believe
You shouldn't be judged
Because of how much you weigh,
And that won't change
It's true
These thoughts will always stay the same,
You're beautiful
At least that's what you've been told
Rather than the size of their souls
People will always be judged based on their looks alone,
You need to be a trendsetter?
Celebrities make you think you need to look better
And by the people you despise
By the ones you idolise,
You're always downsized
No one will ever realise
Beauty isn't skin deep.

Now read this poem from the bottom up.

Kerry Higgins (14)
Dumfries Academy, Dumfries

Being A Teen Is Easy

'Being a teen is easy,'
Adults love to say.
But have they felt tears dripping down their faces
Almost every day?
Online bullying,
It's an epidemic.
The sadness on their faces,
I promise ain't a gimmick.
At least getting punched only hurts for an hour,
But constant aggression can make you feel like a coward.
This behaviour is unacceptable,
There should be no one sceptical.
Or if they want to live
We should give people help,
Make them happy.
Take the crappy feeling away.
So go do something nice today.
Think happy thoughts.
In a happy way.
We need to work together
To get rid of this foggy weather.

It really isn't easy to be a teen
So please... please don't be mean.

Conall Brad Anderson (14)
Dumfries Academy, Dumfries

Homework

I hate homework...

School already takes up half of my life
And when a teacher gives me homework
It feels like I'm being stabbed in the back with a knife
We go to school for a reason.

I hate homework...

What do teachers think I do after school,
Stand around and do nothing like a fool?
I could be doing anything like
Hanging out with friends,
Playing games
Or riding my bike.

I hate homework...

I'm at school thirty-five hours a week
You see school already makes my whole life bleak
But if there's one thing I have learned at school
Is that I absolutely hate homework!

Jacob Hulme (13)
Dumfries Academy, Dumfries

Change

People change people,
They change them to how they see life
But not for who they really are.
They change their looks
Personality and even thoughts.
They want them to be who they aren't.
By changing who they are,
Changes the way they see life,
Changes who they really are.

They tell them,
'You aren't perfect,
You're not pretty,
You're too fat.'
They make them feel
Horrible inside.

But people
Should just accept
The way everyone is,
They should just
Let them be
Who they really are
And not change them
In any way.
Nobody needs to change.

Emma Walter (13)
Dumfries Academy, Dumfries

Enough

They say she's disgusting.
They say it's not beauty.
But what is beautiful when
Beautiful is this brightly lit
Ideal of an unrealistic expectation?

Flat stomach,
Perfect nose,
A gap between your thighs.

It doesn't make sense because
Everything in the media is
Paper-thin models with hour-glass figures
Who are photoshopped until their bodies
Aren't even their own.

We wish we were them
And we wish we were the beautiful thought
Of skinny thighs
And big blue eyes
When all we can ever be is us.
When will we learn that being us
Is enough?

Chloe Duff (14)
Dumfries Academy, Dumfries

Must It Go On?

30 different countries,
Millions of men,
Fighting for their homes,
Their families, their loved ones.

Trenches, guns, bombs and wounds
And sounds of sacrifice,
As lives are lost and guns are shot
And bombs strike through the night.

Their families pray,
Their families cry,
As close friends fear the worst.
But what's it for, these dreaded wars,
Why must they risk their lives?

It's for you and me,
Our future kids,
Our families present and past.
They've suffered in the cold, so we'll grow old,
Must it go on? we ask.

Eve Leonard (14)
Dumfries Academy, Dumfries

Untitled

Is it needed in this world?
It hardly leaves people feeling fulfilled
It's boring, I'd rather be ignoring
I hate it yet people will debate it
Saying it expresses people's feelings
I have a hard time believing
That poetry is about
Believing in more
Saying how you're feeling to settle the score
Believe in what you want
And don't let people taunt
Believe what you believe
And don't dare to grieve
If people say it's not right
Say it's perfect and be prepared to fight
Because everything is wrong
Unless you make it right.

Natasha Biesek (14)
Dumfries Academy, Dumfries

Trapped

These days no one really knows who their real friends are
This is because of social media,
We have around 300 friends on Facebook
If I needed someone
Half of them wouldn't give me a second look,
Nowadays we talk through a screen
We're never fully seen,
Is anyone really listening?
We depend on and crave Wi-Fi connections,
It's not the same as sitting down face-to-face,
This is all our generation has been brought up on
We don't know any different,
Are we trapped?

Lucy Bunney (14)
Dumfries Academy, Dumfries

Heights

Heights, they are petrifying,
My mind believes they are scary,
The struggle is intensifying,
Whilst everyone is all merry.

Diverts me from entertainment,
Feeling nauseous and dizzy,
Now we've come to an agreement,
Heights are a battle for me.

A ferocious enemy to engage against,
May this battle last till the end,
With all this fear that has commenced,
I must now make amends.

Robert Rae (14)
Dumfries Academy, Dumfries

War

War, what is it for?
All the shocking, shelling and shooting
People hating, bullets howling
What is war for?

Lives of civilians lost at what cost?
Armies fighting, terrifying
Bombings right outside your door
This war, what is it for?

War never changes
It's all just shooting at different faces
When will we stop this? It's horrendous
All this chaos, is it endless?

Euan Telfer (14)
Dumfries Academy, Dumfries

All Of You Bullies

All of you bullies, why can't you see
That you're making people's lives a misery?

You constantly bully and seem to not care,
You make people feel like they are not there.

I plead you to stop making people's lives hell,
They feel they've no one in this world they can tell.

I hope one day you get your comeuppance,
I hope someone gives it to you in abundance.

Aidan Cloy (14)

Dumfries Academy, Dumfries

Listen

Heartbreak in the news
Our world is slowly dying
Listen, can you hear that sound?
Children screaming and crying.

We send out lots of brave young souls
To 'make our country proud'
Terrorising, dropping bombs
The screams are getting loud.

Wait, listen now
Can you hear?
All the screams are gone.
Someone else has just
Dropped another bomb.

Abbi Kirk (14)

Dumfries Academy, Dumfries

Missing In Action

It's dark in the forest,
You're surrounded by trees,
You hear a sound,
But you're alone.

You move towards the noise,
It gets louder and louder,
Darkness engulfs you,
It's just you alone.

You reach the noise,
As it disappears,
You search around you,
But you're alone.

The noise reappears,
It's far behind you,
You rush to a lake,
But you're there alone.

You see a silhouette,
It's moving fast,
It disappears,
You're alone.

You feel a presence,
It's close behind,
When you turn
You're there alone.

You see a light,
It's far away,
But then it's gone
And you're alone.

It appears again,
You chase it,
It's gone,
You're alone.

You've reached it,
The forest edge,
A search party,
You're not alone.

They're gone,
The search party,
Just an illusion
So you're alone again.

Deep in the woods,
You're lost,
Missing in action,
You're alone!

Jonathan Hoffmann (12)
Eyemouth High School, Eyemouth

Once Innocent

Knots filling stomachs of the once innocent,
Now remorseful, some malignant with poison in their brains,
Regrets screeching in the daylight sun,
Whether it be a white lie or a murderous rampage.

When life hands out trauma,
Waterfalls break free from sad, expressionless faces,
Turning futile,
Turning sick.

Trembling fingers as the trust flies by,
As with every sin you become closer but further,
Born innocent with a bad brain,
Bang! The pin dropped as loudly as an earthquake.

What is necessary?
Some psychopaths may say, what's right? What's wrong?
The attention-seeking behaviour behind a playful smirk
And the revenge-seeking nature behind the glare.

Regret and sorrow,
Killing people slowly,
But not as slow as the pain in the victim's hazy eyes.

Once innocent,
One decision,
One regret,
One lifetime...

Rosie Mitchell (13)

Eyemouth High School, Eyemouth

The Never-Ending Nightmare

I t never seems to end,
T his is day nineteen of escaping from Sudan.

N ever have I felt so low,
E very step more painful than the last,
V eins throb and blisters appear like magic.
E very meal seeming more like a fast,
R abidly fighting for scraps - it's tragic!

E mma and Mum must be 'up there' safe, so
N ow I'm the oldest, the chief of the clan.
D idn't expect that a few years ago.
E vening is coming: better play the man,
D ig a fire pit, but keep the embers low

S o they won't see
A nd take us children off to fight,
D on't be caught, or your life is done.
L ucky we're together, lucky we're as one.
Y ou should sleep now, sleep, goodnight.

Caleb Bewsey (13)

Eyemouth High School, Eyemouth

Homecoming

The swallow flies quick, gliding,
Over a rippled blanket of blue.
Then he shoots out of place,
A sudden billowing of wind,
Throws him away from his teammates,
Like a penny dropped in the deep, dark ocean.

Now he is alone in the treacherous world,
No shoulder to lean on.
However he knows the route
And despite the hurricanes thrown at him
He still has that glimmer of hope to hold on to.

So there is a rainbow around every corner
And as the sun shines down, he flies on,
Not seeing the ants down below
Who stare up at him, battling through,
Until at last, he is home.

Kate Harwood (12)
Eyemouth High School, Eyemouth

Lost Property

I remember where I was when I lost
that pendant you gave me.
I was standing over your memory, knee-deep in nostalgia
and sinking,
When I tentatively reached for my chest and didn't feel
steel.
Stolen? Slid away, slippery sucker,
Ran away down the drain with clinking footsteps.

I sobbed your nature, felt my gut
Curl up and serve itself like possum, playing dead,
fed me acidic covers of songs already swallowed.
I cleaned up, cleared head, cleared out, ran for the 401,
Which you would berate, state that it 'doesn't hang about'
And I imagine kissing your head on the way out.

I tripped on the shallow shelf of doorway,
made my way to the perforated seat,
rickety as ever, with an ominously empty space beside it,
beyond it some murky beak-scratched glass
and I kick myself, as despite the route I pick for nostalgia,
I will torture my own memories in ways killers would flinch
for.

Shops, cafés, tat, bric-a-brac, village after village,
Before town, restaurant, city, fast-food, department store,
dressmakers, bakers, doughnut, do not enter (hence broken
rules), fools, clues, chairs with backs, with cushions,
wicker of aluminium,
side by side, table for two, where we giggled,
gurgled wine.

Back alleys, backstreets, feet in fours that tread relentlessly
on cobbled yarns, palms pressed, limply or air tight,
each set of fingers forming a different tangle,
Rorschach or piece of string,
every single addition having infinite digits,
Fidgeting in my seat, riveting stories.

I remember everything I didn't think I'd seen when I was
staring at you, but here I am immersed
in needlepoint nostalgia, pressing into the crook of my arm
and filling my blood like thick white sedative cream,
making my left side heavy,
bearing a deceptive heft.

I see the brown snake shifting between buildings,
scars of celestial glass like shrapnel in the fleshy chunk of
sky, simple riverside ambles flood
over the banks and into my eyes,
which grow heavy with water like the grey taint
in the tightly pulled skin of the sky.

Evenings are painfully drawn back, like squeaking drapes
that I wished were silent. I think of greased cotton buds,
of 'fire walk with me'
of the long walks of Van Sant, the glaring eyes of Hitchcock,
the unflinching portraits of Akerman,
the pain of Haneke. Pain.

All these stories we swam in together, and
I swam in the pools of your eyes, but they were salty and
burning, scalding, folding notes to pass, to apologise.
I run my mouth in a screen and run fingers
deep through long and sand-grain hair,
pushed hard yet felt my own scalp,

dug in my nails, drew blood, drew another note
to slide to you, but this time, a different time,
I blame you for insolence, your disruptive absence,
you've skipped class, passed me in the corridors,
and avoided eye contact,
didn't speak to me today.

I sigh the usual indifference, drink the usual wine,
flick the same channels, suck the same lime,
glug the same brown bottles, skip the same pages,
lick the same salt, chew the same glass,
claw the same spot. I imagine you wincing, screaming stop,
me receiving some sick pleasure in the thought of your
concern.

The nights are the worst, abhorrent twilight hours,
where feet should tap, where arms should cradle,
crouched on the edge of oblivion,
I clutch the quilt, and blissfully imagine throwing myself
in front of the 401.

Jack Sheppard (16)
Harlington Upper School, Harlington

Young Love

Looking back there was this one girl, that I loved so much,
Started off smooth like a car, with no clutch.
But I was only the age of 14, how could I love,
She was my angel, so perfect sent from above.
No joke let me tell this story, right from the beginning,
When I first saw her on my mind, oh Lord I was sinning,
My game was too good, to be losing,
I knew I had to act quick, she would move on
And my chances were thinning.

Will I have her as my wifey, was I ever good enough?
I was just another guy on the side, and she was too buff,
Late nights dreaming, forever thinking, will I ever cuff?
Turns out now making an effort, will I always be tough?

If I could go back I would, you know that I would if I could,
I'm not like other guys babe, there's never much love in the
hood,
Baby give me a chance, ride along and I promise I'll be
good,
I'll never forget you, you're the only real love of my
childhood.

Could I get a chance to even talk to her, or was I too
scared?
When I grew up it turned out, I didn't get aired,
I tried all my pick-up lines, I always came prepared,
I made her laugh and over time, love we shared.

We got into so many arguments, broke each other's hearts,
Even though I still loved her, we kept throwing darts,
We were the top couple, number one in the charts,
But now that's all gone, our love is broken into many parts.

Time had passed, I was 16, the feeling was still strong,
She didn't even feel the same way, and we didn't get along,
Every day was a fight, back and forth, just like ping-pong,
I gave up for love and that's why, I'm writing this song.
When she got a new man, I couldn't lie, I was mad,
How could she do this? She knew it'd make me sad,
But I've learnt my lesson, never trust a girl, they're bad,
Hopefully I'll get over it, and one day I'll be glad.

If I could go back I would, you know that I would if I could,
I'm not like other guys babe, there's never much love in the
hood,
Baby give me a chance, ride along and I promise I'll be
good,
I'll never forget you, you're the only real love of my
childhood.

Matthew François (16)
Harlington Upper School, Harlington

Another City Of Mine

The city covered itself with a shimmering sheet,
Knowing that no one would take a minute,
Would take a seat,
Knowing that it wouldn't do much to calm this shining city,
I knew the city was upset,
But I wasn't doing this out of pity:
'I will,' I whispered to the desperate city,
'I will awe at your perfect lights,
I will stare at the perfect contrast between the sky
And the city so bright.
I will peer at every person's walk,
I will listen into everybody's talks,
I will awe at every single sign
And I will remember that tonight, that today,
This city is mine.'

Dhillon Ahira (13)
Harlington Upper School, Harlington

Painless And Strength

I feel no pain
In my veins
Whilst walking
Through the stinging nettles.

Someone punched
Me really hard
The pain will travel to them
And inject them.

I feel like
An anvil dropping
On someone,
My strength is stronger
Than my dad and mum.

Michael Johnson (14)
Harlington Upper School, Harlington

The Cliché That Could Have Been

I think you were the sort of boy
I could have fallen in love with.
Hard, fast, deeply, suddenly, head over heels
or however else you are supposed to fall.

Maybe I could have 'drowned'
in the blue depths of your eyes.
They looked as if, whilst
finger-painting your person into existence,
God had reached down,
and betwixt mighty thumb and forefinger,
pinched a ripple of pure cerulean sea.
Then swirled it around each iris.

The poet in me liked that.

I liked as well, the lyricism of your face.
Your hair, an unruly ink stain,
as black as the darkest simile.
Cerise lips spilt words
I wanted to enclose in this poem,
like a locket: palest ivory
wrought with obsidian ink.

Your laugh was the sound of optimism
plucking on vocal chords
like harp strings.
When you talked,

you savoured each phrase
as if it were fine cuisine,
teasing the flavour out of each
morsel of a sound.

I thought you were beautiful.

And that is superficial, I know.
When you write someone,
you should construct them from inside out.
Cell by cell. Syllable by syllable.
Instead, I have crafted you of
similes and metaphors.

I had not your measure,
and so can only place words against you
as best to work it out.
For that I am sorry,

I will apologise if we ever meet again.

Elizabeth Proctor (15)
Kesteven & Grantham Girls' School, Grantham

A Message

The hardest thing about love
Is how much it can hurt.
Like a fire that burns bright,
And lights up our dark hearts.
Some fires last longer than others,
But all fires fade, eventually
Turning to bitter ash, suffocating smoke.
Yet a fire that burns for a long time
Will settle down slowly,
Slowly until only a few embers remain,
Its beauty dulled, power diminished.

Our love was slow-burning -
It was just meant to be.
A melancholy, wonderful, tragic serendipity.
But I am the only flame left,
Turned cold without your heat.
The time we spent, the moments we shared,
Are more precious to me
Than all the riches in the world,
But no amount of gold could let me see you again.
And, despite the time we had,
All the memories we plucked from the tree of life,
Like perfectly ripened apples,
Delicious, but ultimately finite,
I feel as though I never truly told you
How much I loved you.

So I'm doing it now. Here.
One final message - from me to you.
As I stare at cold words
Etched into cold stone,
Mocking in its finality.
A message from fate,
To me.

Alexandra Tyndall (15)
Kesteven & Grantham Girls' School, Grantham

Bottled

How is it that it came to be?
Our message. Stuck.
Forever entrapped in the glass force field...
That we are told to call home?

Where do we stand
When we cannot stand at all?
When our message is only to be absorbed,
Into the vast abyss,
As others before us have faded.

To suffocate in air:
Is to drown in ignorant bliss.
The slippery, shattered slopes of the truth -
Transparent or just invisible?
Reeking the havoc of the all-knowing light,
Like a fragile pane of glass.
Pure?
Or good at hiding insecurities?

We will not be heard,
Our message, the next message -
The next generation,
Not before our apparent dawning.

They keep us bottled,
Only to drown us in realities that should not exist;
Should they have been heard;
Should a message have been received,
Long ago...

Eleanor Massey (13)
Kesteven & Grantham Girls' School, Grantham

Tongue Twisters!

Help! I think my brain is dead!
These rhyming words go round in my head.
My tongue is tied in a firm knot.
Please can someone make it stop!

My head is throbbing
My mouth is dry
But let me give it another try.

OMG, this can't be true!
I think my face is turning blue
My mouth is about to drop off
I really have had enough!

I want to give it another try
But I'm scared that it might make me cry.
My brain is surely going to burst
I think my mouth might be cursed!

I might blow up in your face
You might think I'm a complete disgrace
But hear my words before I blow
I really wanted another go!

Cara Booth (12)
Kesteven & Grantham Girls' School, Grantham

The Words I Need To Say

Let the words I need to say
Reach the hearts of those I love
Let the words I need to say
Fly upon the wings of hope

Let the words I want to say
Pierce the minds of those who care
Let the words I want to say
Show them all I see and know

Let the words I hope to say
Open the eyes of those now blind
Let the words I hope to say
Craft a message to help folks cope

Let the words I wish to say
Touch the souls of those nearby
Let the words I wish to say
Create a path between friend and foe.

Shannon Beasor (15)
Kesteven & Grantham Girls' School, Grantham

Your World

The world is your oyster
You hold it with two hands.
At times it may seem difficult
And things don't go to plan.
You encounter danger, an immediate reaction.
Its beauty beyond imagination.
What hides inside is the main attraction
Delicate but tough, the world is loved
And what lives beneath the surface
Is precious and meaningful!

Sumitra Patel (11)

Kesteven & Grantham Girls' School, Grantham

Only

If only I'd listened,
If only I'd waited.
If only the danger
Could have been missed.

If only the people,
If only they'd waited.
If only we'd stopped them
This could have been missed.

But we can only wish,
And we can only wait.
For we can only think
What we might have missed.

Daisy Rogers (15)
Lady Manners School, Bakewell

Circus Freak

Yellow eyes that beg and say,
Stay with me, I want to play,
But every smile receives a backhand,
Every laugh, a lash from his grand master,
This isn't fair, he was born like this,
Snakeskin face backed up with a hissssssss,
'Too dangerous for normal society,
Put him in the circus for all to see.'

Clowns and cards will make a good show,
But a circus freak is the way to go,
Tie him down,
Make him fall,
Break his crown
'Cause after all,
He isn't really a man,'
Why can't these cruel spectators see?
He isn't a monster, he just wants to be free,
Understand, you don't know,
What it was that made him so,
He really is just a man.

'Ladies and gentlemen, children of all ages,
Come and see the circus freaks locked away in their cages,'
The contortionist, the giant and the Siamese twins,
'Come jeer and mock them with malicious grins,'
Poke fun at the deformed girl who looks like she will break,

'But she's not really human, so it's OK,'
'Too dangerous for normal society,
Put her in the circus for all to see.'

Trapeze artists will put on a good show,
But a circus freak is the way to go,
Beat her up,
Make her pay,
'It's all her fault, she ended up this way,
She isn't really a woman,'
Why can't these cruel spectators know?
This is her life, it's not just a show,
Understand,
Don't be blind,
Push all misgivings from your mind,
She really is just a woman.

Remember dear, there's a price for cruelness,
Innocence is not the same as ignorance,
Children, children love to watch things burn,
Society, you still have much to learn,
Monsters are always made my man,
A truth you never seem to understand,
The people you give the title of WORTHLESS,
End up being the freak show at the circus.

'Ladies and gentlemen, children of all ages,
Come see the freaks locked away in their cages... '

'Come one and all to see the show,'
It's the only place that the freaks can go,
The deformed girl, and the snakeskin boy,
The Siamese twins, the contortionist toy,
'They aren't really human,'
Why can't these cruel spectators understand?
Their appearances aren't formed by their own hand,
Showing kindness,
Isn't weak,
Someone care for the *'circus freak'*,
They really are just human.

Isabel Lovell (15)
Lady Manners School, Bakewell

Portal To Tír Na NÓg

Through the blue
Through the deep, shimmering, sparkling blue;

Into the Aether
Into the mist
Into Ginnungagap
Into the kiss
The kiss of the elf
Who greets me in there
In the Otherworld
The Otherworld
Through the portal, in Tír na NÓg.

In my dreams I see a portal
Of deep, shimmering, sparkling blue;

Sleipnir the steed galloping high
Frey with his sword riding on by
The ravens of Odin flying up through
Through the World Tree
Through Yggdrasil
In the portal to Tír na NÓg.

The portal, it draws me closer
Into the lake of deep, shimmering, sparkling blue.

And the island in the lake
Holds the true ones so sweet
Ceridwen's stirring her wisdom-filled cauldron
Brighid is burning to see the old one
The Morrigan hov'ring o'er fields of battle
The Tuatha dé of Tír na NÓg.

They're all the same
All linked
Holding the realms together.
The portal to the land
Of dreams, magic and truth.

Just follow the key-lines
Follow the ravens
Follow the gods
They will lead you true.

They will lead you to the portal
To the deep, shimmering, sparkling blue.

Emma Gwynne Ann Pugh (15)
Lady Manners School, Bakewell

Labels

At first I was hesitant
I know that you're thinking
dear Lord we have another one
my confidence starts shrinking.

Yes, I'm proud to say it
I'm a feminist, so what?
At least I'm not a crazy loon
going round smoking pot.

Now I'm not from a cult
I'm not here to rant and shout
don't want to recruit you
men-haters please walk out

so there is a misconception
that you have to be a girl
or there is no more need for feminism
excuse me as I hurl

but how can't you see it?
Baby boys wear blue
girls wear pink,
already they have labelled you.

Women seen as objects
this goes without saying
however it isn't just the men
women criticise, are betraying

raped men, less support
and they shouldn't cry
oh no, society won't allow.
Why not? Because they're a guy

with the patriarchy bearing down
who knows what is right and wrong
it is hard to fight a power
especially one so strong.

Without a doubt, I know
there is a glass ceiling
I deal with it every day
but I'm tired of kneeling

tired of being told 'it's for my safety'
I'm refusing to hide
'Oh you're a feminist?'
to those stereotypes I'm tied.

Now there will always be people
who hate without much thought
but whilst you do some good
behind their safety screens they rot

you may have your arguments
some of them fair
come on open your eyes
and the patriarchies there.

Abbie Franklin (14)
Largs Academy, Largs

Friendship And Fashion

You know when you outgrow your clothes - even your
favourites?
And I find myself thinking, *aren't friendships like that?*
If you and a friend aren't getting on,
It doesn't mean you've done anything wrong.
It just means you've outgrown them.
It's best to say 'goodbye' and walk away
Instead of squeezing yourself into a friendship that hurts.
One day, I will outgrow my favourite dress, skirt and T-shirt
And it will remind me of the friends I loved
And hated so much
'Cause I'll never fit in it again, no matter how hard I try.
Other friendships can be like a game,
And I don't want to win it
If I can't play it my way
I adore my friends, fashion too,
Especially things shiny and new,
But family is the best thing life ever gave

Cerys Robertson (13)

Lodge Park Academy, Corby

The Power Of Driving

I love cars
When I was young all I wanted to do was drive
every day, every hour
because it makes you feel alive
it's all about who's got the most power.

I want to go back to the good old days
where the engine was bigger than the car itself,
didn't matter about torque, G-force or pace
the cars were made of steel not carbon fibre lace.

It was all about power
the power to drive
the power to go
the freedom, the fun
going 150 whilst sitting on your bum.

Now don't get me wrong I love hybrid cars
saving the world and giving Mother Nature some love
I know self-drivers will be second to none
reducing accidents from millions to one.

Welcome to the new age that's what they're all saying
no more queues, no more boredom or anger,
no more waiting.

But when your car is driving itself
it is no longer a car, just a moving shelf
and whilst all we need is an appliance on wheels
a car can be more than that
it should be all about the feel.

The feeling of comfort, of speed and power
of grace and doing over 70 miles per hour.

So you can keep your Toyota Prius
with its hybrid technology and all round smartness.
I'll have a Mustang over that any day, thanks a lot
because when you flex your big toe that car really trots.

So while electric cars may be second to none
when it's driving you and not you it,
how, might I ask, do you feel?
Pampered most likely
but not number one.

Connor Neill (13)
Lodge Park Academy, Corby

Nothing

The day starts great but all fun disappears
When we live in a world full of hate.
You lay your books on the desk in school
When the mean girl pulls out your stool.
You trip, stumble and fall to the floor.
Embarrassed, you climb back up
And say nothing at all.
It's lunch and you head to the canteen,
Your tray is full of food and you can't wait to eat
But yet again she stands in your way and flips your tray.
How can anybody be so mean?
Your stomach rumbles and you start to gag,
You run into the toilets and puke in the sink,
But guess who's behind you?
Not now, you think.
She's stood with her arms crossed
And her followers behind her
And before you know it you're down on the floor.
Kicks and punches are thrown
But you don't fight back, you just deal with the pain.
The bell rings and the girls flee
And yet again you get back up
And go to your next lesson without telling a soul.
It's home time and you're in your bathroom.
You find your mum's pills,
You take not one but ten,

You black out and fall to the floor.
The people watching could have helped
The girl that sat next to you in class did nothing.
The boy that was in the line of the canteen
Right behind you did nothing.
The girls that walked into the toilet
Walked right back out and did nothing
But what can we do?
We can do everything.
At the first sight of bullying tell a teacher,
Friend, sister, brother or mother,
Just tell everybody so we can stop doing nothing.

Shanade Bisland (14)

Lodge Park Academy, Corby

A Cat Is Stray

All alone, without a home,
No matter where you moan,
As you stroll away from nowhere,
You reach the dump, in an emotional evening,
You're invisible to everyone,
You're a stray, without a care.

As you try to sleep, you appear in a nightmare,
With having no more hope for the future,
With bugs and insects crawling in you,
Wounded from the last fear you know.

Before the stray, you would be trapped,
Left behind for months, with no food, no water;
As the men barged in the garden, you waste no time,
You escaped as quick as a flash,
Even though you were nearly caught by his hands in flesh.

All alone, without a home,
No matter where you moan,
As you stroll away from nowhere,
You were spotted by the same men of the past,
As he chased you into the alley he's ready to rise,
As you close your eyes thinking he'll hit you,
Yet he patted you, as you can see his lovely smile,
A smile of hope.

You have been transformed from an ugly stray,
To a lovely creature of a home, meeting nice people,
Nice food, nice cats of hope, who miaowed, 'our souls
Were darkened but now we're heading for hope'.

Ana Jefimova (13)
Lodge Park Academy, Corby

The Difference Between Boys And Girls

He can say what he wants
But she has learned to filter her words
He can do what he wants
She keeps her lips pursed.

He openly stares
She must act like she doesn't care
His words are rude and loud
Her thoughts can never be spoken aloud.

He speaks to others without fear
She flinches when they come near
For he has never had to worry
Yet she's rushing to her home
Every night in a hurry.

Girls mature faster than boys
Because they have been taught
About the dangers that lurk in the shadows.

For if she were to speak
Spews of words would leak
But when she's given the chance
She notices a shake in her hand.
Her throat burns
Soon it's her turn
To speak to the crowd

The crowd of 'friends'
The crowd that pretends
They do not hear her words
They do not know of her 'curse'
But the voices in her head do
They cackle and tell her not to
Not to do this
Not to 'exist'
Not to believe
Will she ever be freed?

Katie Erridge (13)

Lodge Park Academy, Corby

Bullying

You're in school one day
And you're trying to impress your mates,
You don't know what to do,
So you decide to bully.

That time, you screamed 'baldy' to a Year 7 girl,
Her family are in grief right now,
She was diagnosed with cancer yesterday.

That time, you were in the hall,
When you called that boy 'anorexic'
He starves himself because of bullies like you!

That time, when you were walking
To your next lesson,
You punched that guy for no reason,
He suffers child abuse at home right now!

So when you're in school one day
And you're trying to impress your mates,
Don't bully, find another way
To impress your mates.

Kai Campbell (13)

Lodge Park Academy, Corby

Environment!

People sit in a chair,
Made from the wood,
From the tree,
That creates the oxygen that we share.

Some people just do not care.
About the endangered panda bear.
'What do they do?' people may ask,
'It's not like they will do an important task.'

They leave their rubbish on a lonely beach,
But they will face the consequences each.
It fills me with fury to see this sight
And fills creatures with terror and fright.

Boats leak oil into vast oceans,
To see a bird covered in oil messes with our emotions.
People take time to change, time to change these features,
If we help we can save these creatures.

Samantha Annabel Balcomb (13)
Lodge Park Academy, Corby

You'll Never Walk Alone

'You'll Never Walk Alone', the song we chant,
As the red men enter the pitch,
It echoes over Merseyside
And into the air.

Into the air, into the air,
Hoping that one day the fallen ones will hear it again,
'You'll Never Walk Alone', it isn't just a song,
It means you'll always have someone no matter where you
come from.

The amount of red that fell that day,
We will stand outside that Hillsborough flame
And read their name and remember it forever
Because they were the men who went up to Heaven.

Dylan Muir (13)
Lodge Park Academy, Corby

No Right To Poach!

Poaching is never right,
Why take it to such great heights?
Leave all animals be,
Why should we have to make them flee?
You use their skin for decoration,
Plain discrimination.
Trapping protected animals,
Making yourselves criminals.
They are living beings too,
They should be treated like me and you.
Why should they have to run away,
When we should be trying to help them stay?
Think about if you were one,
Always having to hide and run.
Poaching is never right,
Why take it to such great heights?

Kimran Kaur Singh (13)

Lodge Park Academy, Corby

No Two Things Are The Same

No two things are exactly the same...
Two frogs aren't the same
Two dogs aren't the same
Two sunflowers aren't the same
Two cakes aren't the same
Two shells aren't the same
Two bells aren't the same
Two hairs aren't the same
Two hares aren't the same
Two prints aren't the same
Two tints aren't the same
And two people aren't the same
No two things are exactly the same
Everything and everyone is unique.

Chloe Ann Scott (13)
Lodge Park Academy, Corby

Hurt

All backstabbing and pathetic lying,
Sometimes it's just fear.
It can leave everyone crying.
Verbal abuse from corner to corner,
It's like the heat in panic of a sauna
Isolated and alone...
The people you loved now a stranger,
It's all a huge cluster of upset and danger,
Sat alone, feeling glum,
Constantly made to feel dumb,
Helpless and breathless,
Left having no clue what to do,
More thoughts come out of the blue...

Maisie Stevenson (13)

Lodge Park Academy, Corby

Alone

As he sits alone and silently cries,
He's sick of saying he's okay and sick of the lies.
All the names go round and round in his head,
As he has sleepless nights in his lonely bed.
'Loner', 'creep', 'waste of space',
The words get louder as the storm starts to race.
As he sits alone and silently cries,
He's sick of saying he's okay and sick of the lies.

Kaden Carr (13)

Lodge Park Academy, Corby

From Me To You

I am so alone
And nothing feels like home.
I'm so fed up with all of you
And no one cares if I'm down and blue.
I just want to set myself free
From him, from her, from you and even from me.
And sometimes I think what do you mean?
We're all the same, white, black and sometimes green.
So don't make any sudden moves,
Because in court I'll win and you'll lose.

Rhys Rutter (13)

Lodge Park Academy, Corby

Halloween

Knocking on doors,
Cheering, trick or treat!
Holding their bags out to get the most.
'Boo!' shouts a little boy dressed like a ghost,
Groups of teens walking all out in costume,
Skull, vampire, more
Or from that new movie I just saw.
'Suicide Squad' I think it was!

Charley Choina (13)
Lodge Park Academy, Corby

Homeless People

Being homeless is not fun,
Not enough money for food makes you feel glum.
Sleeping in doorways and sleeping on stairs.
Nowhere to go, nowhere to stay,
You slowly start to lose hope every day.
Sleepless nights, snow starts to fall,
Snowflakes become colder as I grow older.

Catherine Clayton (13)
Lodge Park Academy, Corby

Dance!

The nights of training,
Are draining.
The shows come around,
Who knows the moves?
The sound of the feet
Matches the beat on the ground.
Pound, pound, pound.

Amy Dawn Gallagher (13)
Lodge Park Academy, Corby

Fireworks

We were fireworks
Then our flash faded to flicker.
Being jerks,
Being bitter
And then that flicker
Turned to smoke.
Arguing,
Just to give your ego a stroke.
And then we were choking on the smoke
That was once us.
Heart heavy,
I watched us turn to dust.
If you aren't my life-long love story,
If your heart is no longer my territory -
Then I'm glad *we* were the prologue
I'll pay homage to our explosion in the epilogue.

Leah Marie Smith (17)

Luton Sixth Form College, Luton

The Modern Mind

You're in a room.
A black room.
With hardly any light,
It's just you there.
Occasionally voices too,
But they go away,
they'll come back soon again.
There is a wall in front of you;
It's a large screen
It turns on and off.
But the movies it plays,
Aren't pleasant you see;
They're your traumatic memories
Trying to turn it off?
No, you've tried, impossible.

But then,
The screen turns off.
All is black
No light
You see nothing,
You feel nothing.
The voices,
Come back,
They're louder.
You can't silence them remember?
What is this?

Tears?
This is socially unacceptable, you have to stop.
The voices hurt you?
Grow up
Move on
Carry on.
Block everything
Forget everything.
But it comes back?
Forget everything
How?
Somehow, anyhow.

You can't move.
Something controls you
Movement is hard
Impossible.
For each time you move you lose effort,
You lose effort, you lose motivation
No motivation?
Good luck, have fun
You're going nowhere.

The grip is tight.
You're out of motivation
You're out of effort.
People scare you,
The future is pointless
Are you pointless?
Maybe...

Your friends? Do not need you.
Your family? Does not care for you.
They've forgotten.
The future? It does not need you there.
You're just another hay in the haystack, you're not the
needle.
Is life meaningless?
You don't know
Is there a point to anything?
You don't have energy to find out
Is there a point to life?
You
Don't
Know.
Is there a point to life?
I
Don't
Know.

Karolina Zadroga (17)

Luton Sixth Form College, Luton

She Sits

She sits
She sits with her head resting on her palm

She sits
She sits with her head exhausted within her palm

She sits
She sits with her head running through words that make no sense leaking onto her palm

She sits
She sits with her head plugged with ukulele music she prays will not let her sink into her palm

She sits
She sits with her head aching and begging for some sort of release fighting against her palm

She sits
She sits with her head rolling down letters and punctuation, she can't forget the shape of her palm

She sits
She sits with her head about to let into the world of nothing as she is too tired to try and rest on her palm

She sits
She sits with her head that was too exhausted, over used, encouraged yet blocked, trying desperately to not let her heavy eyes turn their keys as she intensely wars against the unforgiving palm of her hand holding her head up

She sits
She sits with her head fallen, warped and outwitted by the soothing pressure of the palm of her hand

She sits
She sits with her head arguing, work, sleep, work, sleep, work, sleep... every option she ends with sleep after becoming too exhausted to think anymore

She sits
She sits with her head fallen, warped and outwitted by the soothing pressure of her hand.

Fiona Green (17)
Luton Sixth Form College, Luton

Copius Wreck

5pm
Family is like the rain
It pours
It lies
It stains.
The rain cascades marvellously
Like a murmuration of starlings flying through the macabre sky.

Oh, won't you wait for me my darling? Please don't go. I'll start to cry
But they refuse to
The raindrops refuse to hold each other.

7pm
The thunder above me bellows
A calamitous shroud descends to play his cello
Tearing the fabric of my world with his doleful melody
Every string strung echoes my inescapable destiny

12am
The rain pours.
Scatters
Inundates
But the rain doesn't remain shoulder to shoulder.
They deny holding each other's boulders
Even though

They all brace for the same intimate collision with the
Ground,
Ready to embrace the soil,

To plunge into the ocean.

They sink in.

2am
These drops were once content in a cloud of no calamity.
Now they are a broken and dissolved family.
Problems will never be solved
Because their happy cloud popped.
And they will never care enough to...
Sigh.

5am
An infinite amount of care was all we ever need to survive
But the precipitation of cold, wet drops of tears and strife
Is all it ever was.

5:30am
Rain isn't the most joyful thing and neither is kin.

Shamia Khan (16)
Luton Sixth Form College, Luton

Seasons

In winter the snow is falling down,
It's cold so we give a frown.
But we can still have fun outside
Because there will be snow far and wide.

In spring the flowers come out to shine,
It's getting warmer, is that a sign?
We can get a football and go outside and play,
The days are getting lighter, so we are out all day.

In summer lots of people go abroad
But if you stay at home, go to the beach and have some cod.
In summer you can get really hot
So put some suncream on but not always a lot.

And last of all, autumn, the leaves fall off the trees,
It's a lovely sight for you and me.
Sweep all the leaves on the floor,
They might keep falling so that makes more.

Cameron Stewart (11)

Mearns Academy, Laurencekirk

A Poem To My Brother

When my brother tells a pun
I really think it isn't fun,
His jokes are the ones I like
And when he does my day goes quick,
Like I'm on a bike!

I love my brother through thin and thick,
I'll share an ice lolly, take a lick.
My brother really thinks he's funny,
Or should I say he's very punny!
He is very lazy.

In the morning it's very hazy,
As usual I look outside, oh look a daisy!
I'm going downstairs to eat Shreddies,
Then he comes and tells a joke,
It gives me giddies.

Going upstairs, just to chill,
TV time! Let's watch Harry Hill.
Another joke, another bad time,
His jokes are sometimes as painful as juiced lime,
It's like a burn to the eye.

He just tells too many, then I cry
But maybe I'll laugh 'cause that's a good one.
If it's not I'll scream as loud as a gong.
When that scream hurts his ears
He says cheers!

Morgan Le-Tekro (12)
Mearns Academy, Laurencekirk

Norse Myths

Odin, god of war and death killed his father,
Giant Ymir, he lay down his body in space,
Body became tree known as Yggdrasil,
World tree.
Odin created nine worlds,
Each connected to tree,
Asgard, Vanaheim, Nidavellir, Álfheim,
Midgard, Svartálfheim, Helheim,
Jotunheim and Muspelheim.
Odin had two sons,
Thor and Loki,
Gods of thunder and mischief.
Loki killed stepbrother, Balder,
Telling Balder's brother, Hod,
He was a giant.
Odin foresaw Ragnarök,
Twilight of gods.
Surtr, lord of fire giants,
Would unbound Fenris Wolf with Samarabrander, Freya's
sword
And burn the nine worlds and all gods.

Harry Coleman (11)

Mearns Academy, Laurencekirk

Meow And Mow

They had a show called Meow and Mow.
They both are cats and they're made from Play-Doh.
They love rolling around into little balls.
They have their own theme tune.
They're no longer on TV
But you can find them on YouTube.
Meow is the green one, Mow is the red one.
They're always outside rolling around in the grass,
They hide in the bushes as well.
As a kid it was hard to fit in
But the show showed me how.
Me and my sister loved watching it
And we still do.
We love it!

Ella Geddes (12)
Mearns Academy, Laurencekirk

Lights Of New York

Lights flash, red, yellow and green.
These are the lights of the city,
That is New York.

Big, busy, bright,
These are the flooded streets,
The streets that are like rivers,
Never slowing or quickening.

Colossal, mighty, strong,
The famous things
That are skyscrapers,
The windows like tiny shards of glass.

And last but not least,
The massive square of green.
The place that squirrels call home,
The place that is Central Park.

Rhianna Grace Morgan (12)

Mearns Academy, Laurencekirk

Titanic

Titanic
Hit by an iceberg, sailing to America.
Collided with an iceberg, sinking fast.
People scramble to lifeboats,
Leaving the poor to suffer.
Staff tried to help calm people down,
People started to drown.
People begging for help,
Nothing came, people slowly died.
The rich, sitting nearby, watching the ship sink
And listening to the children scream for help!
After two hours the ship was gone,
Everyone gave up.
There was no more Titanic.

Erin Hair (12)

Mearns Academy, Laurencekirk

Tragedy Of Twin Towers

To the dead,
To the living,
To the families,
To the friends,
To those who remain,
Who remain mourning the tragedy it was.
The smoke,
The fire,
The memories,
Will go down in history,
As the immoral event of the Twin Towers,
Of the terror,
Of the loss,
15 years.
We give our deepest sympathies,
An unjustified action,
9/11.

Josie King (12)
Mearns Academy, Laurencekirk

Two Days Before Christmas

November or October
This tragic event started
Admitted to hospital with jaundice
But soon realised she had cancer
Over weeks it spread
Until it reached her brain
Then she got confused
And forgot where she was
And then two days before Christmas
It was a tragic day
She said goodbye to us all.

Kirsty Gellatly (11)
Mearns Academy, Laurencekirk

Barney

His soft furry skin
How I miss having you
How he got so thin
He died and a part of me did too
I certainly miss having a bunny
You were my ups and downs
Sleep tight, my baby
Robyn loves you loads
And always remember you will never be forgotten.

Robyn Jane Fowlie (12)

Mearns Academy, Laurencekirk

Cheerleader

Jumping, stunting, tumbling,
Competitions,
Ground shaking,
Teeth chattering,
Adrenaline filling,
Amazing,
Fantastic,
Throwing, flipping, toe-touching,
Cheerleading,
My team,
My squad,
My second family.

Erin Spence (12)

Mearns Academy, Laurencekirk

Me!

Dark brown hair
Greeny, blueish eyes
October 18th 2004
Video games
Pizza
Annoying little sister
Mum
Dad
Small white cat
Fleetwood
Auchenblae
Mearns Academy
Golf
Alex Clarke!

Alex Clarke (11)
Mearns Academy, Laurencekirk

Football Goals

Football goals every day
Can't wait for them to replay
So get off your seat
And watch that defeat
By your team today.

Cameron Barclay (12)

Mearns Academy, Laurencekirk

Titanic

Titanic
Frozen colossus
Unsinkable ship

But on April 14th 1912
1,517 died
In that icy sea.

Max Miller (12)
Mearns Academy, Laurencekirk

The Dark And Cold Inside

It's dark, it's cold,
But I can't grab a hold
Of what I truly need.
What I need would be like a good deed,
What I need is light,
What I need is bright,
What I need would be good,
'Cause right now I'm stuck in the mud.

When it's dark
You just want to make your mark,
When it's light
You just don't want to fight,
For someone to come
And take all your sun.

Then it's dark, it's cold
And it's written in bold
That you're not who you used to be,
When you were you and I was me.
Now it's light
With delight,
So now it's time to fight,
Your fright.

Caitlin Lewis (11)
Outwood Academy Newbold, Chesterfield

I Wonder 'Bout A Life

I wonder 'bout life,
I wonder 'bout it all,
I wonder 'bout taking a knife,
I wonder 'bout sharpenin' a saw,
I wonder if it would be crazy.
If I had mo' ladies,
Cause right now I'm being lazy.
I'm at the end of rap game,
The game was driving me insane.
But if I quit it would be lame
So I'm gonna stay.
Been doing this a while and now I've found my style,
Got into this 'cause of 8 Mile, so cried to Eminem.
It's time to go home, home again.
I may be free once again.
I gotta run away, 'cause right now, where I stay
I cannot last another day.
These people drive me insane,
No wonder I joined the rap game.
Yeah, it takes the pain away.
Hoping I can get his trust again
Before somebody takes it away.
I'm about to go on holiday to find what I seek,
Try not to be weak.
Try not to speak for a week,
That is the challenge in hand.

Those are my dreams, don't fret.
This ain't a threat, I don't deserve the criticism or compliments,
This is who I am, this is what I do.
Outside of this land I don't have a clue.
They call me lost but this is the place I was found.
My hands are empty, I'm home now.

Bailey Ethan Astle (14)

Outwood Academy Newbold, Chesterfield

I Promise To Deliver...

As I stand on the podium giving my speech
I'm craving your vote just like a leech.

I promise an end to all that is bad
To follow the good like my forefathers had.

I can deliver all this and that
To feed the hungry and slim down the fat.

When I'm there at number ten drinking champagne
And thinking again.

And all that I said I was going to do
For him, her, them and you.

It's all gone to pot
I've forgotten what I promised.

I'm living my dream thanks to the voters out there
Who now shout and scream.

Bethany Louise Parsons (14)
Outwood Academy Newbold, Chesterfield

Butterfly

If I could be any creation
I would be a butterfly
No brittle need for preservation
Or endeavours gone awry.

Her wings of benevolence softly
Float before admiring eyes.
She enchants with innocent beauty,
Imbued with chaste exercise.
She endures no difficulty
But her rich yearning for flight.
Her emancipation engulfs her
With sheer and opulent light.

If I were she, no trepidation
Would swarm when the end was nigh
Diaphanous manifestation
Shattering without a cry.

Alas, I'm no butterfly.

Abigail Khan (16)
Outwood Academy Newbold, Chesterfield

Wonderland?

If time doesn't stop, I'll be late
The stopwatch will chime
And I'll be strung up like a puppet
Being controlled from the shadows
Unable to break free with nothing but a smile on my face
It isn't fair
Alice was able to control everything in Wonderland
Everything should be under my power
But there is one problem among all of this, my dear
And that is that this isn't Wonderland
And you are not Alice.

Ciara Davies (17)
Outwood Academy Newbold, Chesterfield

Memorial
(In loving memory of Lee Griffiths)

A limb has fallen from my family tree,
Yet no matter how emotional the thought may be,
We grieve not for him, all our lives instead,
Reminisce, remember the best of times.
We cherish the laughter and the song,
Every word that rolled from his tongue.
And of course the good life he lived while he was strong.

Nyesha Davies-Collis (12)
Outwood Academy Newbold, Chesterfield

My Best Friend

You are the 'cheese' to my 'toasty'
You are the 'warmth' to my 'fire'
You are the 'apple' to my 'tree'
You are the 'paper' to my 'plane'.

You are the 'crust' to my 'muffin'
You are the 'your' to my 'nan'
You are the 'best' to my 'friend'
And the something I can't say because it's just too rude.

But it's you,
Remember that time we watched a funny video
And you hit your knee.

Remember that time we were making Minnie Mouse
Pancakes and you read the packet and laughed so hard
You fell on the floor because it said, 'Seize the crustize!'

You are the 'source' to my 'E'
You are the 'beardy' to my 'man'
You are the 'rare' to my 'productions'
You are the 'Peter' to my 'Pan'.

You and I have lost friends
And found friends
Been the weird friends
And been the loud friends.

But no matter what, you are my quirky, loud, sporty, pretty,
Make-up-obsessed, funny, smart, kind,
Helpful, musical, happy, sunny, tanned friend.
No! Best friend.

And, I know in my heart and can feel it when you're near,
That there is something there, but I have no fear.
Because I know, and that this is true,
Charlie would be proud of you.

He's always watching, always there.
Always proud, always fair.
Always that robin, way up there.

You are my best friend, my very best friend!

I couldn't ask for anyone more.
Never think you are anything less
Because you are my best friend,
My very best friend.

Phoebe Taylor (13)
Redborne Upper School & Community College, Ampthill

A Child's Mind

A child's mind cannot fit in a box.
It cannot be recorded on paper
Nor can it be expressed by voice alone.
Restrictions put on harmless creativity
Could condition them against what they are here for.

When I was younger, my father,
He wanted me to tick boxes.
He attempted to squash anything
Vaguely linked to creation,
Imagination, anything I need to express,
To represent me... as a person.

Two minutes in his company
And the butterflies, I imagined that grew
In flowers on blue trees on a hill, flew away.
My head left blank and concrete,
Constantly being graffitied by his own insecurities,
Personality, ingraining my mind
With lines drawn with rulers in red pen.

I preferred the squiggling lines,
The exciting lines,
The lines that twist and curve
The same way a vine climbs a fence.
A fence made of straight lines,
Because a child's mind is supposed to
Embellish what their parents try to teach them.

A child's mind is full of endless possibilities
As they have yet to be taught that they cannot
Fly on wings of their own.

Now this, this is not a poem supposed
To belittle academic minds,
The minds of people who don't believe
They can draw or make music or write.
This is a poem to show how
A child's mind needs to be free...
Because without the minds of children,
Instead of saying we cannot fly...
They made someone think to try.

Lauren Campbell (16)
Redborne Upper School & Community College, Ampthill

Big, Bad Brexit

Brexit, honestly, why are you here?
Your awful ideas have ruined my year.
The scale of your stupidity, is really quite large,
Seriously Britain, why trust Farage?

The state of the Earth is seriously bad,
But you're just erasing the hope that it had.
The EU has helped us; why would we leave?
Or is it just losing money, to those who are in need?

Let's face it, our parliament is wrecking our future,
We may as well be ruled by a hyper headless rooster.
They want to evict our free NHS,
When they finally quit, there will sure be a mess.

What our country has worked on for a century and a half,
To take it away, you're having a laugh.
As we leave, into an uncertain outcome,
The country's nervous heart, is beating like a bass drum.

They say that time made the human race more clever,
But someone new to this theory, would not believe this ever.
Our brains have been improving for millions of years,
The concept of Brexit: evolution's worst fears.

So just like our country, this poem must end,
The number of poems you've read by now, I shan't
comprehend.
You've made it this far, and my whole poem has rhymed,
I hate to disappoint you, but this bit doesn't.

Archie Walker-Merison (13)

Redborne Upper School & Community College, Ampthill

Corruption

When I was small,
I wanted to live.
See the world,
I wanted to give.
Yet when you fully open your eyes,
You come to realise
This isn't what you had in mind.

Prince Charmings hide behind Tinder profiles,
Swipe right, you swipe left - for none seem...
Worth it.
Buy this, buy that - but remember kids!
Natural is better,
No one will love you if you're ugly and bitter.

Eeper Weeper, chimney sweeper,
Why don't you become a wife beater?
The police won't know,
There aren't any left.
Tear gas isn't the only thing to have you cry,
And seem bereft.

Humanity it sobs, screams and bellows,
Singing its song against Mother Nature,
Her body ruthlessly violated; hacked at and dug.

All we wanted was freedom.
All we needed was love.
Why couldn't you hear us
Till it was too late?

Our children sit in dirt, deserted
Men and women seek each other's hands for last goodbyes.
Phones smack and fall,
Screens go black,
Watching missiles make comets through the skies,
A star without a wish.

It's over.
It's done.

Our era has ended
With the barrel of another smoking gun.

Lucy Gouldthorpe (16)
Redborne Upper School & Community College, Ampthill

The Last Day Of May

The day I met you we danced until the sun replaced the
moon
In the end a mutual agreement, although it was too soon
Romance ran out of time
The moon doesn't want to shine
I can only stand here and remember the thing we said and
did
Acting like teenagers, acting like kids
You still have my heart no matter the outcome
Although I'm starting to wish this romance had never begun.

You have half of my heart
The part I have is beating fast while it crumbles slowly
I used to worship you like you were something holy
The powerful sound of my mind racing at the thought of
what I might say if I see you again
I wonder exactly what have you done, stayed sane?
You threw my love on the train tracks and destroyed your
love for me
You took the love I had for granted so easily
I'll never be able to love like this again, I should have held on
What did our failed fate rest upon?

Leaf by leaf they will fall as time passes by
You're laughing, singing and thrill-filling while I just cry
I know you haven't thought of me since that day in May
It's about time I got rid of the skies that are painted grey.

Megan Kemeny-Ruff (16)
Redborne Upper School & Community College, Ampthill

A Night Out With Friends

'No, let go!' He slams the door.
You're not going.
Not anymore.
That scantily clad? You look like a w****
You must never forget that oath that you swore
What's with him? He's sweet, but never before
Have we been locked in this game of tug or war.

It's always like this, the rope won't break
But my hands are burned, my palms just ache.
Was it all me? My little mistakes?
My resolve is now weak and I'm going to break
This is not him, but I refuse to partake
In this game that he plays, that he plays for his sake.

I'd pull first, but with one pull back
Brings me to him, knelt or bent back
Subdued again, he fades to black
A slap on his wrist is a pretty attack
Now I've made up my mind, my final tug back
To move out from that door, get my life back on track.

Now it's time for this game to end
From this violent pit, it's time to ascend
You'll never see me, never again
Now without food or money to spend
I'm leaving, I'm going, I'm making amends
And all of this, for a night out with friends.

Rory McGowan (17)

Redborne Upper School & Community College, Ampthill

A Bad Day Made Worse

7:35, you'll be late for school
And the essay you were going to do; it's due.
Due first lesson, your worst lesson.

8:14, you leave for school,
Then get splashed by a puddle.
Signal's down on your phone,
No friends to see, alone.
A blocked nose from hay fever
And today it rains, you shiver.
It was hot yesterday; the weather told you wrong.
Stay strong.
You have your friends,
Forget loneliness.
Walk along, stay strong.

Then you arrive at a scene of chaos
To find your best friend's your loss...
She became your best friend instantly,
Now she leaves, abruptly.
'I'm going back to America,'
But you're my primadonna!
'I'm going back,' physically impaled me,
Visceral pain.
Like a vital part of your body, gone:
Your legs, your eyes, your lungs.
'Don't go,' you force,

I thought lung capacity was a renewable source.

You leave for school
And get splashed by a puddle.
Walk on, stay strong.
For your best friend, who's gone.

Georgia Cope (17)

Redborne Upper School & Community College, Ampthill

War

Skin saturated with sweat.
Hairs standing up in anticipation.
Eyes an ocean of rage and ravenous hunger for 'justice',
As if seeing the world through an angry red filter.
I am resolved,
I am ready and willing
To do as I have been told.

White knuckles from a closed cold fist.
Eyebrows - a knot carved into your forehead.
Thoughts of home and family are lost,
It is time to lock away childish thoughts.
I am resolved,
I am ready and willing
To do as I have been told.

You're not thinking clearly anymore but that doesn't matter.
Just go for the kill.
Your unsteady hand finds the trigger,
But your parents didn't raise you to be like this.
I am resolved,
I am ready and willing
To do as I have been told.

But what happens once the storm begins?
Once no-man's-land becomes a brown blanket blemished
with bodies?
Blood may pulse through open wounds,

But your fate is surely sealed.
I am resolved,
I am ready and willing
To do as I have been told.

Emily Campbell (16)

Redborne Upper School & Community College, Ampthill

Time

You can't always see it,
Perhaps it's not even there,
Time.
Does it exist?
Or is it a fundamental lie,
Purely created to scare?

Deadlines,
Running on time,
Punctuality,
Why?
Just take a moment to stop.
Watch the world pass by.

Question it.
Think about it.
Take as much time as you need.
What would you do if time was no object?
What could you achieve?

Unwritten books,
Worlds unexplored,
Skipping out breakfast - it doesn't have to be more.

It defines us,
Tangles us in chains,
Time of birth,
Time of death,
Pictures held in frames.

Seconds - tick!
Minutes - tock!
Hours - tick!
Days - tock!

Built up, it becomes more,
Decades, centuries,
Opportunities gone, ignored.

Take some time,
Sit there - just be you,
Ignore the clock,
Or watch it tock,
Imagine what you could do.

Hollie Hansen (16)
Redborne Upper School & Community College, Ampthill

Inequality

This is for the people who suffer with inequality.
Why should people suffer if they're a girl
Or they're in poverty?
Just because two sides are different
Shouldn't mean they start a war.
We should all get along
Even if we're rich or poor!

Why do we discriminate about other people's race?
What has this world come to?
It's a disgrace!
Why should people be bullied
About how they look?
Maybe they should think about
How their soul will be shook!

Why do we ignore the values
That we should share?
Some people are starving,
But some of us don't care.
What a world we live in.
Hate, crime and sin
What is the point of inequality?
Just put it all
In the bin!

Colette Joy Russell (13)

Redborne Upper School & Community College, Ampthill

Finding Myself

Bullying is the root of all evil.
People snigger, and people sneer.
Pick on the woeful girl who is alone,
Just because she has an identity of her own.

Worthless and lonely, these are the words I hear,
You are yet to know, you're my immense fear.
My bleeding heart is still on the mend,
The only thing I wish for is a true friend.

Now I am free, I am no longer alone, I am free.
Those nasty insults no longer sting me.
Being bullied, gave me power and stability.
Always remember, words are nothing but stupidity.

I have found myself, I have also found freedom.
People can be poisonous and unpleasant.
You can always find the worthiness in people.
Don't ever tolerate the evil.

Maizie Sherwood (15)

Redborne Upper School & Community College, Ampthill

Untidiness

Untidiness is awful,
Untidiness is hateful,
Untidiness is definitely
Not my friend.

Cables are a key contender,
One here, one there,
And all I want
Is that one there.

Paper is a messy one,
Not straight and in the way,
I wish it would not crease
As it ruins what you are trying to read.

Pens and pencils are one of the worst,
Unstraight or partly used,
But the worst thing
Is when they are chewed or cracked.

One last of my hates
Is by far the worst
Which is things that are unstraight,
Books on the desk,
Posters on the wall,
In fact anything
That is not straight
Does not please me at all!

Toby Smith (13)
Redborne Upper School & Community College, Ampthill

After Effects

I hate the way you're happy without me.
I hate the fact you're doing so much better.
I hate that you seem to be everywhere.
I hate that I put a lot of time and effort into you.
I hate how you're friends with my friends.
I hate how I can't bring myself to hate you.

I loved the way you were happy with me.
I loved the fact you were doing better because of me.
I loved that you were everywhere I looked.
I loved that you put your time and effort into me.
I loved how we were friends with the same people.
I love how I loved you.

But what I hate
And love the most,
Is how I can't bring myself to hate you,
No, I'm not even close.

Lara Denise Fisher (17)
Redborne Upper School & Community College, Ampthill

Toy Soldiers

They are just toy soldiers
Walking into battle, singing songs
They are just toy soldiers
No lives are lost, they're simply marching on.
When one breaks, it's just replaced
Discarded bodies, gathering dust
Wave upon wave, they line up straight
Ready to be knocked down like dominoes.
Emotionless faces, opaque eyes
Watching as the next row dies.
No room for difference
They must all conform
It's one big package
With a matching uniform.
Across the field the ranks of foe
Bearing the same weapons
Wearing the same clothes
Assembled by unseen hands.
Who will mourn their loss?
They are just toy soldiers.

Edie Wright (13)
Redborne Upper School & Community College, Ampthill

A November Poem

Leaves are falling every day,
Grab a rake and rake them away.

Summer's long gone, winter's near,
I cannot believe Guy Fawkes is here.

Watch the colours light up the dark sky,
It will be bright for the rest of the night.

Grab your coats and lots of friends,
And here is hoping it will never end.

The fire is out, Guy Fawkes has gone,
And that is yet another year gone.

The trees stand empty, the grass stands cold,
The animals hide, otherwise they will look too bold.

They store their nuts and berries deep,
And hope that no enemies do peep.

David Fussell (13)
Redborne Upper School & Community College, Ampthill

Stages

It starts. With the headaches
Then the backaches
Eventually everywhere. Just. Aches.

You then feel, the tiredness
Constant loneliness
Soon to be lost in. All. This.

You've come to accept
That you have not slept
For months upon end
You promise this isn't a trend.

The rope by your door...
The gun on your floor...
The blades in the bath...
Creating a blood path...

Although I seem fine
(An overused phrase of mine)
I want you to forget
Everything I just said

Starting from the day
I said I was okay.

Olivia Thomas (16)
Redborne Upper School & Community College, Ampthill

Labelling

Stop labelling people for how they look,
Or how they do in school.
They may be smarter than you think.
When you say those rude words,
It causes people to sink.

Do you think it doesn't hurt?
Don't make someone feel like dirt.
Airhead, dumb, stupid and nerd,
Pain can be caused by a simple word.

People are labelled, whether they're fat or thin,
There's nothing wrong with the colour of their skin.
Ugly or buff,
What even is this stuff?

So stop the labels and the stereotypes,
Don't believe all the hype.
Give someone a chance
To do right.

Sofia Villa-Buil (13)
Redborne Upper School & Community College, Ampthill

Homophobia

I'm sitting here alone
Watching the seconds tick away,
Thinking there's one thing to me that's unknown,
Why do people discriminate against those who are gay?

Why can't some people understand that a man can love
a man,
And a woman can love a woman?

No one chooses the life they are given,
But with it, they did their best,
In their heart they listen to their rhythm,
Their life is not yours to test.

Some people's lives are full of sorrow,
Simply because they are in love,
So I'll wait here until tomorrow,
Like I'm in a cage like a dove.

Amy Scott (13)
Redborne Upper School & Community College, Ampthill

The Beautiful Game

Football, the beautiful game.
Scoring goals, gaining fame.
Though it's not all gain and fame,
It's also a respectful game.
Day by day training all day,
Sometimes failing but trying again.
Doing what it takes to take a win
With top-class fans, supporting the team.
On the match day derby with the smell of burger and chips
With the sound of fans having a chant-off.
It all sounds perfect
But it's really quite not.
There is still one thing left,
It's really bad.
Racism.
It doesn't matter if you are black, white or red,
All you should do is enjoy the game.

Kade Alford (13)
Redborne Upper School & Community College, Ampthill

Battle The Bullies

Bullying isn't clever,
Bullying isn't cool!
Maybe it's best to stick to the rules.

Naming and shaming isn't for me,
Maybe just stick to watching TV.

Somewhere deep inside you
There's something good within.
Use that instead and don't do the wrong thing.

Words can hurt, words can make you feel sad!
If you use them incorrectly
They can make you look bad!

Violence isn't the answer,
Violence isn't good.
Treat people how you want to be treated
And you'll be in their good books.

Maddy Jenny Chesham (13)
Redborne Upper School & Community College, Ampthill

Bad Weather

Waking up in the morning to the freezing cold
Before you know it it's thundering like hell!
Boom, boom, boom!
Then in the click of your fingers it turns pitch-black
There is nothing left but the loud storm.

The sun may come out to say hello
But not for long...
Here comes the wind blowing your hair,
This weather is like a dice rolling in the air!
Swoosh!

I hate the wind, the rain too,
But when the sun comes out it is a hello to you.
Bye bad weather, stop ruining my hair.
Boom, swoosh!

Debbie Fridkin (13)

Redborne Upper School & Community College, Ampthill

Untitled

Excuse my outlandish request,
I've tried to listen, truly,
But when it comes to you, dear,
This impropriety must end.
You've truly got it wrong this time,
How can you not understand?
Sweetie, I hate to be the
One who has to break it to you,
You being my partner does not
Justify this pitiful
Behaviour of yours, love -
Why do you never hear my words?
It's not just me who's picked up on
Your cruel demands; don't worry,
Some day you'll get it, pumpkin,
Karma is coming back for you.

Corren Perks (18)
Redborne Upper School & Community College, Ampthill

London

Emerald thistles tore their way through the pavement,
Whilst herds of people marched on by.
Several one-bedroomed flats available to rent,
Covered in realms of ivy and vines.

Neat rows of freshly planted flowers
And the subtle scent of pine trees.
The hectic atmosphere slightly overpowers,
The beauty in which London releases.

The densely smoke-filled air,
Flowing in and out of people's lungs,
Is occasionally hard to bear,
Filling their throats and stroking their tongues.

Ellie Camp (18)
Redborne Upper School & Community College, Ampthill

Why War?

Smoky air but who's to care,
There's more to worry about just like war.
People dying young and old,
People trying to hold their ground.

Blood is filling the soil below
Flooding from the stone-cold bodies that lie below
While others are forced to watch them die
And the worthless sit there and cry
So please tell me why
So many souls have to die
And why some cannot just let others live their lives
Without war and death
And making it really seem like we are living in Hell.

Ben Seber (13)
Redborne Upper School & Community College, Ampthill

Victims Of Cancer

Cancer is harsh, cancer is cruel,
People are fighting a violent brawl,
Friends and family all around,
And still yet a cure to be found,
As cancer doesn't let your children grow up,
Though you can help her do her make-up,
It crowds, surrounds and makes you feel isolated,
When you can't remember what you just contemplated,
From breast to lung cancer
And different types of cancer it has yet to cause,
From smoking to nothing at all,
It definitely doesn't deserve a round of applause.

Fraser Lamb (14)

Redborne Upper School & Community College, Ampthill

Three Open Letters To The Three Worst Fears I Wish To Conquer

You will not get the best of me.
I will squeeze you by the throat.
Grapple my way into your existence
And throw you down the stairwell.

There are a hundred things I wish to lose,
But oh god, not you. Not you.
I could never lie to you, and I will not,
Let you go, I will swallow you whole.

Sometimes, I grab the weight with a fishing hook
Pull tight; let my arms fall back like a lost pendulum
And wait, patiently, for the crash.
I never knew you were pushing behind it.

Kaiya Kaltio (17)
Redborne Upper School & Community College, Ampthill

Bullying And Self-Esteem

The noise of the footsteps growing louder and louder,
I just started feeling prouder about myself,
I'm in horror, I'm in fright,
This is why I'm scared of the night.

Words can hurt, punches too,
I'm a human being, I have feelings
Everyone comes in different shapes and sizes
That is what makes people special.

I hear the sound of teasing and crying
I see children running and hiding
I want to stop the fear that is in them
I am brave and confident.

Reece Collins (13)
Redborne Upper School & Community College, Ampthill

The Apartheid

We are all the same,
Nothing different,
Only our colour,
That was the problem.
We lived in one area,
They lived in another,
Why weren't we allowed to cross?
Because it was the rule.
We were educated here,
They were educated there,
Why not together?
Because that was the rule.
We caught this bus,
They caught that bus,
Why not the same bus?
Because that was the rule.
That was the rule,
That was the apartheid
And I didn't like it.

Ella Cope (13)
Redborne Upper School & Community College, Ampthill

Poetry

Poetry, what's the fuss?

Teachers expect us to think that it's a must.

What's the point of teaching it?

Most people don't remember it.

It's just a song put into words of rhyme

About love, culture, rap and crime.

You may as well be doing things that will help you understand,

Instead of filling our brains with poetry... it should be banned.

So when your teacher starts this topic

You sing this poem and say stop it!

Harvey Sweetland Jones (13)

Redborne Upper School & Community College, Ampthill

Fear Poem

Fear, fear, fear is in the air,
Fear is everywhere,
In the air, in your hair,
On the ground, underground,
Over ground, in your head, in your bed,
In the night or in the light.

Fear is everywhere, where's your fear?

The human eye picks up more than you think,
A simple blur can become a creature,
A simple shadow can become a demon.
Can you take on your fear?

Nathan Eaves (12)
Redborne Upper School & Community College, Ampthill

Expect Of Me

Sitting at my desk,
Checking my Instagram,
Wondering what people expect of me,
I'm pretty,
I'm thin,
I'm kind,
That's what they all say,
But that's only today.

They expect me to love him,
But I don't at all,
They expect me to be mean,
But that's not who I am,
They expect it from me,
But I'm myself inside...

Jasmin Susan Clark Batchelor (13)
Redborne Upper School & Community College, Ampthill

Leaving The EU

We are leaving the EU, off we go
We won't have any allies left when we fight our foe.
We are leaving the EU, off we go
We don't have any infrastructure though.
We are leaving the EU, off we go
We can't get any friends because of our stupid parliament though.
We are leaving the EU, off we go
They say Britain is a stronger country alone but then Nigel Farage goes.

Luke Smith (18)

Redborne Upper School & Community College, Ampthill

McDonald's Heaven

Some just call it McDonald's
I just call it Heaven
Some just call it unhealthy
I just call it tasty
As you walk through that glass door
The options are just more and more
And those special machines that do the work for you
And then you wait for your order
Scope out a table that the cleaner just cleaned
And then you eat your food more than pleased!

Nathan Wing (13)

Redborne Upper School & Community College, Ampthill

Wealth

Sport, it's all a game,
The players get all the fame,
Also with the big amount of money,
The poor don't earn any,
The rich, should help the poor,
That could mean the world would have more,
There would be more shelter,
To protect people from the bad weather,
Also more enjoyment, to spread across the world,
The world can become wealthier!

Connor Andrews (13)

Redborne Upper School & Community College, Ampthill

Bad Weather

I hate bad weather,
The worst thing is how
It can change whenever.
From sun to rain
And snow to storm
All I want is to be home and warm.

Hot chocolate in hand,
Tucked up in bed,
Visions of sunshine
And bees in my head
As the weather outside,
Gets wetter and wetter
I'm all tucked up
In my cosy sweater.

Sofia Samm (13)
Redborne Upper School & Community College, Ampthill

Cheerleading Is Always An Option

1, 2, 3, 4
Cheerleading is an open door,
5, 6, 7, 8
You will always have a mate.
Throwing people in the air,
Live your life without a care.
1, 2, 3, 4
Dip so you can keep the roar,
5, 6, 7, 8
Cheerleading is a sport I rate!
We'll be the winners as we walk off the stage,
With sass and class,
No matter about the age.

Rhiannah Webster (14)
Redborne Upper School & Community College, Ampthill

Depression

As the sadness takes over my brain,
All I feel is pain.

As I start to cry
I feel like I want to die.

I always get blamed
And now I'm sitting in the rain.

Trying to explain
When I really want to complain.

Now I have a stain made of my blood,
Wishing that I could be up above.

Tia Lawrence (13)
Redborne Upper School & Community College, Ampthill

War

I woke up,
Then the bombs fell from the planes up high
And then the sirens went off.

The sky lights up,
The gunshots roar!
My mum shouts at me to run,
I say I want to fight
So my mum leaves me behind.

I grab my AK-47 and my M1911 and go to war!
One shot to my head and I'm on the floor.

Tyler Swain (13)
Redborne Upper School & Community College, Ampthill

Free Running

I have many hours in my day,
When I sit and think,
How I'd like to spend my free time,
Free running is on my mind.

When I go out my body gets a rush,
I try new things eager to be the best
And strike to win every contest,
With Adidas shorts and trainers on my feet,
I know I'm someone no one can defeat.

Christopher Dadd (13)

Redborne Upper School & Community College, Ampthill

Life Of An Abandoned Dog

Here I am,
Chained and alone,
I sit in this circle
I made on my own.

It weighs at my neck
And weighs at my soul,
I feel like I'm dead
And they're digging my hole.

Just bring me inside,
Let me lay at your feet,
Even after all this worry
It's you I want to meet.

Kate Devonshire (13)

Redborne Upper School & Community College, Ampthill

A War

The sound of explosions
The sight of death
Family homes crashing down
In the south-west
These images projected on our television screen
But some images are just unseen
Of those who've lost families, friends, husbands and wives
Caught up in the misery and lies
A war of whoever loses dies.

Harvey Turner (14)
Redborne Upper School & Community College, Ampthill

Line Of Fire

Fields of spilled blood
Trenched through the thick mud,
A shower of bullets,
A tower of bodies,
Strife of death,
All in deep depth,
Without any reason,
Full of treason
For none will ease on.

Joshua Tuuk (13)
Redborne Upper School & Community College, Ampthill

Go-Karting

Karting, race to the lights
From beginning to end
From start to finish
Everyone needs racing
Everyone needs sport
Karting's all I want
Karting's all I need.

Henry Treanor (14)

Redborne Upper School & Community College, Ampthill

What Does It Mean To Love?

Love is not just a verb inside,
Love is a word forever misused.
Love is a word not used enough,
Does love even exist?
I'm starting to think love is just a myth,
Factions bombing innocent people whenever they wish,
Crying Syrian children, their homes now a ditch.

Policemen shot another to the floor,
How many lost figures are we 'bout to endure?

The definition of love in this poem follows the story of a
young Hispanic boy:

Love can be lost from the word you hear,
'Cause words can hurt,
They linger in your mind,
They play on your mind,
They crawl down your spine,
You can never seem to leave them behind.

The young boy from the fearless city knew
What it's like to grow up in a place full of verbal abuse.
It's hard when he's let into the world loose.
To people who look like they have it all.

Because his mind is damaged.
He dreams as he sleeps,
A dream full of happiness and peace,
A world where in the future he wakes up to a daily feast.
A happy life.
A successful career.
A happy family.

He wakes up to raised voices on the landing,
Foreign tongues screaming and demanding.
Sexist curses hanging in the air,
No surprise to the woman, no genuine despair.
His younger siblings cry, no more can they bear.

The father does not understand, the father does not see,
That what he says to the mother, affects the children cruelly,
Their childhood scarred forever,
Although they try and shake it off, 'whatever'.

To him love doesn't exist,
To him love is just a myth.
To him women are weak.

Because his mother never dared to speak,
Against his abusive father,
Why does she never leave?
Why does she still believe
In love in a world like this?
She really needs to get a grip.

The reality of this world is that eternal unconditional love is impossible to achieve with all the hate in this world.

Nation rising against nation,
Wars and rumours of wars.
Isn't it better that the world just ended,
It seems impossible for the world to be mended.

But didn't Jesus say to love one another,
To treat people like a sister would a brother,
To love everyone like a son loves his mother.

Let's ask ourselves what it really means to love?

Jadesola Bejide (14)
St Paul's Catholic School, Leicester

Be You, Be Happy!

Why should I be a clone and deal with all the grief
When all I really needed was a little self-belief.
A little less of you and a little more of me
So I can break free from the shackles of this modern-day
society.
And for all my Afro-Carib girls, why can't you see
That having long straight hair doesn't make you any more
pretty.
I wanna do things my way and I wanna have the biggest say
In what I wear and what I do,
After all it's not always about you.
So what if my edges aren't on fleek,
I don't care if you don't like how I speak.
It takes a lot of courage to stand out from the crowd
I don't see many people with a lot of confidence around.
The penny farthing never got us very far
But the penny in that thought got us a car.
So stand up for what you believe in and have your say
Because after all I just wanna do things my way.
So be you and be happy!

Rosa-Mei Wright (12)
St Paul's Catholic School, Leicester

Life Without A Price

Life.
It's crazy
Kids die
Mums cry
It happens daily
Wondering if their kids out there got safety
Like I said you know
Life's getting crazy.
Sailing by, see youths
In blue tracksuits
Like warships, it's crazy
More guns that the navy
The bigger picture
They can see (sea)
They are too busy thinking that they're wavy
Soon be in jail 'cause of trapping
Locked in his cell, now he's trapped in
A street soldier
The streets feel colder
Massive chip on his shoulder only makes him bolder.
Ghost'll haunt them when they spray Call of Duty
Kill a guy in cold blood
Like they've been called for duty.
The war getting ugly ain't nobody seeing beauty.
Discriminate
'Cause of a colour of the face,

I don't rate that
Getting revenge,
It's not over like the Drake track.
Police shoot innocent guys
What can we say to that?
Kill a guy
And parents get no justice
Parents left reminiscing
Left thinking, *what's this?*
Kids not coming home
Well then I guess it's cheerio
If they see a serial killer
Should've listened
When Mum said,
'Don't,' like Bryson Tiller
Kids don't have models to follow
So they run away tomorrow
A pocket full of drugs
That's a hard pill to swallow.
Gangbangers on the streets
With that gun play
Guns and violence
Shoot a guy
You'll get left for dead today.
If it's like it's a game
It'll get mortal
Then there's bare combat

It's a fatality
Then you won't come back.
Aim high, you can evolve
To anything
Big house
Nice car, kids maybe
Even a wedding ring
Give yourself a goal
You can score
Be the opposite of poor
First you gotta learn
Then you can take the L off.

Tendo Gumbo (15)
St Paul's Catholic School, Leicester

Untitled

Bring yourself up, don't keep yourself down,
put a smile on your face, not an ugly frown,
don't think of failure, just believe in yourself,
work very hard and you'll be the best.

You can fight fire with only your fists,
if you try your best, you'll never miss,
you can climb the whole ladder in a short space of time,
you will never give up and be the master of rhyme.

You can solve anything with just your mind,
there's this inner self-motivation that you will find,
you'll be sitting at the top, looking at everyone below,
but only, if you work hard though.

Determination, that's what you need,
after success, it should be knowledge that you'll feed.

Umar Patel (12)
St Paul's Catholic School, Leicester

Legacy Over Currency

Just like a donkey chases that shining carrot stick,
now it seems like humanity is chasing only one thing
and you all know what it is... money,
that precious thing that revolves around our economy
like a turntable and rustles through our fingers
as dead leaves, as some of us 'make it rain'.

Why don't we ever want to embark on leaving a legacy?
Well, you tell me.
Not chasing those dollars or yen, pound or euro,
my precious mind is only focused on leaving a legacy,
by that you'll remember me.

But why; you tell me,
will the generations after me recognise *me*
for the great impact I made on the world,
or the money I spent on things that only had value to *me*?
Just know I want to leave a legacy.

Idolising money has been engraved into the heart of men,
whilst the idea of a legacy fades away.
Poof... we can't see it no more?
Recognise that no matter what you do
you will be remembered for it
by the thousands or millions.

You see, Steve Jobs did not just create the iPhone
the billion dollars he saw in revenue,
but the legacy he would leave behind revolutionising
technology.
Did *he* not put his legacy over currency?

Did he not place people over a profit margin?
He left a legacy and we remember him today
by texting on our iPhone every minute.
By my legacy you shall remember me!

Remember you shall be remembered
by the impact you have made on the world
and not by the amount of money you have sourced out of it.
Legacy over currency!

Aiden Clayton-Crosse (14)

St Paul's Catholic School, Leicester

They Told Me I Could Fly

They told me I could fly.
I feel like I could fly.
No, in fact, I can fly
I will.
Rush, rush, rush.

The monster is coming towards me.
The tracks stretch out for miles.
The platform light blinking,
Stand back.

I can feel the gaze of a passer-by,
Burning through my skin.
I step out.
They told me to.

I'm prepared to fly over the monster.
They said I can do it.
I can see it now.
Rushing, blinding light coming towards me.

I can almost feel my wings
Piercing through my shoulder blades.
I step out further.

Rush, rush, rush
I listen to them.
I leap out.
I'm flying!

For a moment I think I can fly.
Rush, rush, rush
But I can't fly
I'm not flying.
They lied
They always do.

I was told not to listen.
But,
I could have sworn they were talking
Just a minute ago.

They told me I could fly
And I thought I could too.
But I can't
I couldn't.

Now all I can see is
Black, black, black
I guess they were wrong.

Greta Kaur-Taylor (14)
St Paul's Catholic School, Leicester

Why Do We Worship it?

We worship it without realising.

It watches us but doesn't have eyes.

It sounds like a stalker but we're the ones who follow it.

You used its power to read this poem.

It doesn't need you but you need it.

You spend most of your time with it but you hardly remember its name.

It's probably closer to you than family.

It's probably behind you.

It has your details.

It could be bad for you but you're addicted.

Whatever it tells you to do, you do it.

You might be more obedient towards it than you are to your parents.

It controls your idols.

It is corrupt but the corruption satisfies you.

I never knew that you could love something that you don't know a single thing about.

But who am I?

Could I be under its control?

It appears that when we can't understand or interpret things, they're scary.

You want to avoid it, don't you?

If that is so true then why do you allow it to take advantage of you?

I'm guessing that you read this poem and asked many questions as a result.
This is my question;
Is it really entertaining or is the media a cult?

Adam Nemat Bhatti (13)

St Paul's Catholic School, Leicester

Holly

A bundle of fluff,
black and white.
Keeps you moving
day and night.
Soulful brown eyes behind a curtain of hair.
When I need a friend, she's always there.
A bundle of joy,
a bundle of fun,
a bundle of trouble,
a bundle of love for everyone.
Older now,
calmer now,
grumpy now!
Quieter now.
That loving heart is slower now.
Those big brown eyes are dimmer now.
She's no longer the dog she used to be.
Old age has caught up for us all to see.
Sometimes, just sometimes,
when the mood takes her,
we see a glimpse of the younger her.
She's ill.
She's fast,
she's slow,
she's old.

Every second is precious to me,
for one day she'll just be a memory.
My dog, Holly.

Rhiannon Kennedy (13)

St Paul's Catholic School, Leicester

Don't Judge A Book By Its Cover

Why is it that we're always taught about the Queen,
But not enough of Martin Luther King?
Why is it that some do drugs,
But the others are expected to get jobs?
All the blood and bones in the soil,
Of all those slaves which made our lives toil,
All the unequal salaries and no spoil,
Leaving us black people in poverty; such turmoil.
All lives matter, yes that's a fact,
But the way our race gets treated clearly shows some don't
know that.
What's that they all chat?
It's a 'misunderstanding', mate please don't chat!
The hatred is real, what a shame,
Well that's all I've got to say today,
All lives matter, let us show that today!

Chantelle Nyasha Giwa (13)
St Paul's Catholic School, Leicester

Ghost House

He walked along the uneven path,
Up towards an old spooky house,
Also known as the ghost house.
The people at school said, 'Don't be a fool
Or you will get eaten by the ghoul.'
But he didn't care,
He was only a bit scared
As he walked along the uneven path.

As he opened the door
He saw an old wooden staircase.
The whole house was as dark as a cave.
The door slammed behind him.
His heart raced, it was terrifying
As he opened the door.

As he walked up the old wooden stairs,
Creak after creak after creak.
As if he just stepped on a bunch of mice.
As he walked up the stairs he stopped and stared
At a ghost which peered at him
As he walked up the old wooden stairs.

As he ran out of the house he struggled to open the door,
So he gave it a push and a pull
And, 'Boo,' shouted the ghost
As he ran out the house.

Charlotte Schofield (12)

St Peter's Independent School, Northampton

The Final Round

The final round of the tournament is about to begin,
I can't believe the position I'm in,
There's only one more game that I've got to win.
And the championship's title will be mine for the year,
And all my friends and family will cheer.

The battle begins when the clock is pressed,
My opponent looks calm while I feel so stressed.
A few hours later the game is fairly drawn,
Then all so suddenly he blundered a pawn.
But then I look at my clock with a frown,
Because my time is slowly ticking down.

I'm starting to feel quite sickly
And realise I've got to finish this quickly.
I set a trap and hope he takes the bait,
Smile as he does and I offer my hand with the word
'checkmate'.

Max Miller (13)
St Peter's Independent School, Northampton

The Sun

When I wake up
The sun is shining
As the day progresses
It continues to shine
Even when I am down
It continues to shine on me

When my day comes to an end
It gives me a beautiful glow
As if to remind me
Tomorrow is another day
Yes, when I awake again
The sun is shining

No matter what I am doing
The sun will always shine
Over and over again
The sun will always shine

The sun will always shine for me and you
Forever the sun is our jewel
The jewel that brightens the day
A wonder you are - sun.

Takudzwa Mshayavanhu (12)
St Peter's Independent School, Northampton

Unique

Unique, unique,
No one can beat
Unique makes me feel alive
It's not a crime,
Funny I should say
It's not my mistake.

Unique, unique,
It's as hard as a good beat,
Apples are unique in so many ways
So are you
No one's a mistake,
Lemons are sweet,
Not like feet,
It's your time to shine
In these few lines.

Come along to the Busta Rhyme
Take time and make it shine.

Keisha Dera (11)
St Peter's Independent School, Northampton

The World

The world, in space a mystery
How did it get here
And where did it come from?
A magnificent gem floating in space,
Spinning and spinning like a tornado,
Around the sun it goes.
I don't think it matters that it may be small,
Compared to some of the other planets.
It's green like a leaf and blue like the sky,
Inside the Earth there are many mysteries to uncover.

Devlin Cattermole (11)

St Peter's Independent School, Northampton

Being A Teenager

I know it's difficult.
You feel like everyone is against you
And tries to stop whatever you want to do.
There's pressure from Mrs Leech
Or maybe it's old Mr Speech.
The homework is overdue
Or your sister hates you too.
A friend turned an enemy
Or an enemy turned a friend.
Mum says, 'Turn that frown upside down,'
But you leave the room without a sound.
The school bully ruined your night
All because of your stupidly oversized height.
Maybe you develop a crush
Just to discover he's gone in a rush.
It feels like today
Just isn't your day.
So what sums you up?

T eenager
E veryone judges you
E verlasting humiliation always follows you around
N o clothes you find good enough to wear
A nger towards anyone who ruins your day
G ullible towards the school bully
E namoured in an absurd crush
R egretful for all those things you wish you could take
  back.

This may all be true
But look at it from our point of view.
You're only a teenager once
So suck it up and carry on with your life.
Don't let one worthless thing bring you down
Get back on your journey and don't turn around.
Keep your head up high
And don't you dare sigh.
Try not to lose your way
Like a needle in a gigantic stack of hay!

Jessica Smith (12)
The Kibworth High School, Leicester

The Monster

He looked at him from the stair,
Nobody knew what he felt for him,
Would anybody even care?
Shaking hands and breathing hitched,
The boy was two steps closer,
To his heart needing to be stitched.

He didn't know the outcome, nobody did,
Would there be heartbreak?
Would there be tears?
He was shaking,
Oh he was so scared,
He was one step closer,
To his heart needing a repair.

The fear of rejection,
The fear of despair,
The fear he'd be called queer,
The fear the boy wouldn't even care.

He was crying now,
He was on the bottom stair,
He was 0 steps closer,
To his heart needing care.

The monster stood before him,
Giving him a stare.
The monster stood tall

Just like the boy's hair.
The monster growled and gave him
An inquisitive stare.

He took a deep breath
And blurted it out.
A question full of passion
And most importantly doubt.
The monster smiled
And ran a pale hand through his hair,
Then embraced him in a hug,
Full of passion and care.

He looked up and smiled,
A monster was no longer there,
It was the boy he adored,
With bright blond hair.

Laura Smith (14)

The Kibworth High School, Leicester

My Perfect World

I dream of a world where hate is denied,
Where love is eternal and always supplied,
I would love a world without human greed,
Poverty abolished, where no one is in need.

No anger, jealousy or envy, no worry, hurt or pain,
A world not driven by Insta-likes and everyone wanting
fame.
Where the elders teach the youth
And the youth are respectful too.
Where everyone has a voice
And every voice is free to share its view.

Where true beauty lies within and no one need judge,
Arguments are to be forgotten and no one retains a grudge,
Even toddlers gain forgiveness and respect is taught at
birth.
A world without crime, where everyone is safe on Earth.

Where all hopes are to be fulfilled,
The aspirations of the youth, to build
Where there is no racial discrimination
Where people can finally accept that we are a multicultural
nation.

There's women out there fighting for equality
Trying to abolish the majority's superiority
Young girls fighting for their education
Just trying to change society for their generation.

Sophie Grove (14)
The Kibworth High School, Leicester

Syria

War after war, do we never learn?
It tears us apart like the rubble of a shattered home,
Blown up by our selfish deeds
And the heart's darkest desires.
Brutal ideology exposed to the glare of the world,
Played out each day on our screens,
A multitude of images,
Whilst we sit in the comfort of our homes.

A fragile child, dust as a blanket,
Lies cowering in what's left of her precious home;
Once a safe haven of love and security,
Surrounded by her family and neighbours.
Now a pile of concrete,
Metal fingers pointing to the sky.
Family dead, injured, missing.

Civil war;
Family fighting family and friends fighting friends.
Senseless, hopeless, the loss of a nation.
Selfish and cruel, the consequences delivered at the end of a
bomb.

Can we ever learn?
If we learn from our mistakes,
If we change our ways,
Breed peace and not hate,
Then maybe!

Rachel Danielle Modha (14)
The Kibworth High School, Leicester

Poaching

Listen carefully to this grizzly tale,
That I'm about to tell,
Its truthful heartbreaking sadness,
I'm sure that you will know.

A tiny lion running through,
A sundried savannah,
She's small and little
And her name is Hannah.

Here comes the poacher,
With his rifle,
He aims and shoots
As his sons are eating trifle.

Luckily the lion isn't hurt,
But he is badly cut,
He can't run very fast,
Because of his injured foot.

The poacher shoots again,
This time it is a hit,
The lion falls right over,
if only he had a first-aid kit.

The poacher goes on home,
With his little son,
If only he could be wise,
Then maybe we all could've also won.

Rowan Guy (13)
The Kibworth High School, Leicester

Give And Take

I give you fresh free air to breathe,
You give me sinister smoke to suffocate on.
I give you shimmering bright light,
You give me horrible daring darkness.

I give you gleaming beauty,
You give me useless unfair ugliness.
I give you everlasting love,
You give me hideous heartbreaking hatred.

I give you an orange glinting dawn,
You give me a penetrating sunset.
I give you life-changing medicines,
You give me nothing but injuries.

I give you an adventurous life,
You give me a cruel dark death.
I give you free exotic animals,
You give me unfair extinction.

I give you brilliant new discoveries,
You give me frightful fur coats.
I give you peace, perfect peace,
You give me distrustful war.

Emily Bettinson (12)
The Kibworth High School, Leicester

Military

People give their lives to protect us,
Navy, army, air force.
It could've all started on a school bus.
Iraq, Pakistan, anywhere they are,
They aren't forced.

They chose to risk their lives,
They leave their family and loved ones.
They sacrifice everything for us,
To live, to survive,
To have hope.

You may think it's lame,
Or that they need a new brain.
But they do this for us.

They love us, protect us, believe in us,
But then they are,
Worried for us, scared for us.

I don't blame them to be honest.
You go see what they've seen,
Will you be honest?
Saying it's lovely, it's nice?
Or dangerous, deadly and lethal?

Louise Kyle (12)
The Kibworth High School, Leicester

Pet Poem

Hamsters are…
Squiggly, wriggly, balls of energy.
Dogs are…
Bouncy, friendly, bundles of fun.
Cats are…
Cute, fluffy, want to play.
Horses are…
Big, grand, they love to run far.
Fish are…
Slippery, fast, fascinating to see
They are all unique just like you and me.

However…
They don't like being ignored.
They don't like being sad.
They don't want to be not cuddled.
They don't want to feel bad.
They don't want to be neglected.
They don't want to feel left out.
They don't want to be hurt, inside or out.
They don't want to feel like they're not wanted,
Remember you're their best friend.

Hannah Davey (12)
The Kibworth High School, Leicester

Stand Together

We need to make a stand,
To understand
And help those in need,
Can't you see?

You don't need to be afraid,
We can be a part of this
And make sure no one is alone,
Conquer the lands which to many are unknown.

It doesn't matter who you are,
Where you live,
You can make a change.
Even to just one person,
It can make everything different.

Mental health,
The stigma attached to it,
That is the enemy.
In a number of many,
Let's stand together,
And maybe we can clear the world of this,
Forever.

LJ Hensman (15)
The Kibworth High School, Leicester

My, Myself And I

2016, alone, afraid, everyone
Drinking and drugs, everywhere.
Mental health, diseases, anywhere
Is there such a thing as a good society?

Drinking in the streets, messed
Up everything, disgusting,
Smoking anywhere, upsetting
Young, desperate, lost.

Tears, fights, people,
Arguments, fights, hurt,
Disappointed, scared, normal,
There's no such thing as normal.

Good society - is there such a thing?
Happiness, smiles, love
Love is the reason we carry on
We don't need a good society to fill our hearts.

Mbaweme Zimba (14)
The Kibworth High School, Leicester

Killed In Action

Bullets flying through the air
As the dead man's eyes stare
Looking but not seeing
Any other being.

His family at home eagerly wait
Not knowing his return will be late
Hearing the news, they break down in tears
Scarring their hearts, for all their years.

All his friends he left behind
Will always have him on their minds
Waiting to welcome him back, their mate
Unaware of his unfortunate fate.

The last thing he heard on that tragic day
Was the sound of the guns as his life ebbed away.

Ben Sturgess (13)
The Kibworth High School, Leicester

Animals Have Feelings

Animals have feelings, animals have rights,
What did they do to you to treat them like this?
Left all day, battered and bruised,
Waiting for you, for love, for food.
But that never comes.
Abuse, neglect, cruelty
Is all that comes from your evil little hands.

Try as you might to stop, to apologise,
Your pet never forgets. You must realise
All he wants is to walk, to run,
But all he gets is a kick up the bum.

Eliza Parsons (12)
The Kibworth High School, Leicester

Achieve

The story of the underdog,
Never failing to clear the fog,
Clears the mist of the impossible,
Making the unknown accessible,
Leicester City - beating the best,
Triumph over the rest.

David vs Goliath,
Beating the unbeatable,
David stood tall, unscathed,
The biggest evaporated,
The smallest exclaimed.
Fear, inspiration - it has it all,
Destroying all guarding walls.

Andrew Constantinou (12)
The Kibworth High School, Leicester

Bullying Advice

Bullying isn't nice,
Bullying isn't right,
Those who are getting bullied should get some advice,
Tell someone close,
Who loves you the most,
Tell someone at school and they'll sort if for you,
Whatever you do,
Don't be shy,
Otherwise that bully will have caught you like a fly!

Rebecca Humphrey (12)
The Kibworth High School, Leicester

A Piece Of Cake...

A piece of cake is all I need
To get me through the rest of the day...
I can't wait for the sweet smell
As soon as I hear the bell...

A piece of cake is all I need
To get me through the rest of the day...
All that jam and cream
Makes me wanna scream...

A piece of cake is all I need
To get me through the rest of the day...
That yummy slice
I don't care about the price...

A piece of cake is all I need
To get me through the rest of the day...
On that expensive china plate
I eat it with my mate...

A piece of cake is all I need
To get me through the rest of the day...
No matter what mood I'm in
I never put it in the bin!

Wherever I am...
Whatever the time...
A piece of cake is all I need!

Demi Hart (12)

Westbourne Academy, Ipswich

School Production

In my school we did a play,
We laughed and smiled every day.
We were happy and were sad,
And the play wasn't half bad!
I loved my school play!

I was Bugsy Malone,
The gangster loved by loads.
I was hired by Fat Sam,
And had to fight Dandy Dan.
I loved my school play!

Well I was an egg,
I fell off a wall and broke my leg.
I was raced to Hickory A&E,
Where two flirty doctors looked after me.
I loved my school play!

I was a goat,
That wrote a ransom note.
Shooting with my slingshot,
Working for my boss at the Porridge Pot.
I loved my school play!

In my school we did a play,
We laughed and smiled every day,
We were happy and were sad,
And the play wasn't half bad!
I loved my school play!

Bailey Devereux (12), Freddie King (12) & Taylor Bullard (12)
Westbourne Academy, Ipswich

The Beautiful Game

The ball flies through the air
And nobody has a care,
The calls to get the cross
And the keeper with a toss.

When the card comes out,
The keeper comes about,
The coach does the shouting
And the defenders do the poaching.

The player hits it with his boot
Or you could say he decided to shoot,
The gaffa is loving it
And the striker has a hit.

The keeper dives,
Let's hope he survived,
They have their strongest team
And are still very keen.

Samuel Bell (12)

Westbourne Academy, Ipswich

YOUNG WRITERS INFORMATION

We hope you have enjoyed reading this book – and that you will continue to in the coming years.

If you're a young adult who enjoys reading and creative writing, or the parent of an enthusiastic poet or story writer, do visit our website **www.youngwriters.co.uk.** Here you will find free competitions, workshops and games, as well as recommended reads, a poetry glossary and our blog.

If you would like to order further copies of this book, or any of our other titles, then please give us a call or visit **www.youngwriters.co.uk.**

Young Writers
Remus House
Coltsfoot Drive
Peterborough
PE2 9BF
(01733) 890066
info@youngwriters.co.uk